DISASTER BY DEFAULT:
Politics and Water Pollution

Frank Graham, Jr.

DISASTER BY DEFAULT
Politics and Water Pollution

With a Foreword by Harry and Bonaro Overstreet

Published by M. Evans and Company, Inc., *New York*
and distributed in association with
J. B. Lippincott Company, *Philadelphia and New York*

Second Printing

Library of Congress Catalog Number: 66-11167

Manufactured in the United States of America

Designed by Edward Gorey

Contents

Foreword

Webster's *New World Dictionary* describes the *Domesday Book* (usually called *Doomsday*) as one "that spared none and judged all men without bias, like the Last Judgment." *Disaster By Default* might well rank as a kind of *Doomsday Book* for our times, for it records mercilessly but with complete fairness things done that ought not to have been done and things left undone that ought to have been done; and it concludes that there is little health in us not threatened by pollution.

Perhaps no subject of vital importance to our life, liberty and pursuit of happiness has been less discussed—and less intelligently discussed—than what to do about the deadly accumulations of disease-breeding filth that increasingly menace our health and our life. We know that these lethal accumulations run through our sewers and out into somewhere. But as we step across the manhole, we don't know what is happening, of good or evil, beneath our feet, or what ought to be happening.

"There is no sales appeal in sewers," our author quotes from *Fortune* Magazine. Far less is there political appeal. For sewers, properly built and serviced—with disposal plant and all the rest—cost mountains of money; and no political aspirant is likely to go out to his constituents, hat in hand, for a sewer handout.

Least of all is there any educational appeal. Sewers smell; and educationists quite naturally don't like to invite bad smells into the classroom. (Unless the smelly things can be called acqueducts, which gives them a Roman dignity.)

Nor do the huge and growing industries that line our lakes and rivers and turn them into filthy sludge look happily upon the vast expenditures they would be called on to make in order to clean up the filth they create.

This is the paradox that besets us: as our power to create the good things of life grows greater and greater, so does our power to destroy the very life that creates them.

How can we arouse the good sense and protective good will of our pollution-threatened society? This is the problem that must be met head on if the paradox of breeding enormous danger through enormous growth is to be resolved.

It is books like Frank Graham's that can help us to resolve the paradox, for the book tells the score.

It is a story of public apathy, private cynicism, and ineffective legislation. Obviously there is no cure for such maladies as these except what Teilhard de Chardin calls "the instinct which tells us that, to be faithful to life, we must *know*."

Disaster By Default is "faithful to life." The facts are horrendous—witless, conscienceless, and utterly without excuse. But the book tells them all, honestly and helpfully.

While we were reading the manuscript of the book, one of us remembered a seemingly pointless question with which a philosopher friend of ours began one of his lectures. "What is the difference," he asked, with slow deliberation, "between an archaeologist and a garbage collector?"

He proceeded to answer his own question by saying: "Civilization could survive without the archaeologist."

This book completes the answer: "But not without the garbage collector."

HARRY OVERSTREET

BONARO OVERSTREET

Preface

The author of this book is neither a scientist nor an engineer. He is simply a reporter with a deep interest in conservation. Several years ago, seeing the scars inflicted on the Pennsylvania countryside by certain strip miners, he was made aware of the enormous problem America faces in its conservation of natural resources. He became interested in the menace presented by polluted waters, and in the fascinating dilemmas it poses in both politics and public health. In that discovery this book had its origin.

The story unfolded here is not, or should not be, a secret. It was open to anyone who had the curiosity and the time to uncover it. Most of the facts were gathered from the transcripts of Congressional hearings and Public Health Service conferences, United States Government publications and newspaper reports. Though that material has been supplemented by private interviews with scientists, engineers, and federal and state officials, this book is based on the public record. The polluters are indicted as effectively by their own words as by government evidence.

Following is a list of the government transcripts on which the author most heavily relied:

Proceedings of the National Council on Water Pollution (sponsored by the United States Public Health Service) Washington, D.C., December 12–14, 1960.

Hearings on Water Pollution Control and Abatement Before a Subcommittee of the Committee on Government Operations, House of Representatives, May, June, and August, 1963 (three volumes).

Water Pollution Control Hearings on the Water Quality Act of 1965, the Committee on Public Works, House of Representatives, February 18, 19, 23, 1965.

Comprehensive Study (Interim Report) of the Great Lakes–Illinois River Basin, August, 1961 (Department of Health, Education and Welfare).

Transcripts of the Conferences on the Pollution of Interstate Waters, conducted by the United States Public Health Service, at the following places:

St. Joseph, Mo. (Missouri River), June 11, 1957.

Omaha, Neb. (Missouri River), First Session: June 14, 1957; Second Session: July 21, 1964.

Kansas City, Mo. (Missouri River), Decembers 3, 1957.

New York, N.Y. (Raritan Bay and Adjacent Waters), First Session: August 22, 1961; Second Session: May 9, 1963.

New Orleans, La. (Lower Mississippi River), May 5–6, 1964.

Transcripts of the Hearings ordered by the Secretary of Health, Education and Welfare, held at the following places:

Sioux City, Iowa (Missouri River), March 23, 1959.

St. Joseph, Mo. (Missouri River), July 27–30, 1959.

Because a report on America's polluted waters touches on so many fields, the author's background reading was too extensive to permit him to mention all the books included in his research. He must, however, pay his respects to the writings of Rachel Carson, Fairfield Osborn, and Stewart L. Udall, who have contributed so heavily to the cause of conservation in our time. He must also mention several books on which he relied while writing Chapter Two of this book—that which deals with the historical background of his subject. These include:

Blake, Nelson M., *Water For the Cities.* Syracuse University Press, 1956.

Daley, Robert, *The World Beneath the City.* J. B. Lippincott, Philadelphia & New York, 1959.

Hopkins, Edward S., and Schulze, Wilmer H., *The Practice of Sanitation.* Williams and Wilkins Company, Baltimore, 1954.

Imhoff, Karl, and Fair, Gordon M., *Sewage Treatment.* John Wiley & Sons, Inc., New York, 1956.

King, Judson, *The Conservation Fight.* Public Affairs Press, Washington, D.C., 1959.

Leigh, Robert D., *Federal Health Administration in the United States.* Harper & Brothers, New York, 1927.

The author also wishes to express his indebtedness to various articles and columns in the *New York Times,* the New York *Herald-Tribune,* and the Washington *Post.* Invaluable also were articles by James Ridgeway in the *New Republic* and the series of articles on pollution in the Raritan Bay area by Ian McNett in the Perth Amboy *Evening News.* The New York Public Library, by making available its collection of 19th-century pamphlets on sanitary engineering, contributed to this book.

The author also wishes to thank all of those people who, by kindly contributing their time in one way or another, were of immense help. While he cannot hope to list all of them, he would like to single out Paul De Falco, James R. Harlan, Robert S. Hutchings, Keith Krause, Morton A. Lebow, Sam Levinson, Margaret T. Mitchell, Murray Stein, David G. Stephan, Adrian Sybor, and Kenneth Walker, all of the United States Public Health Service; Leon W. Dupuy, Dr. Ray Erickson, Tom Evans, and Dr. Raymond E. Johnson, all of the Department of the Interior; Representative John Blatnik of Minnesota, Charles Callison of the National Audubon Society, H. V. Fraley of the Caterpillar Tractor Company, William E. Guckert of Pittsburgh, B. C. Harding of Thomaston, Maine, Rolf Hartung of the University of Michigan, Julius Kaikow of the City College of New York, Senator Edmund S. Muskie of Maine, Dr. M. Graham Netting of the Carnegie Museum in Pittsburgh, Dr. William J. Ronan, Secretary to Governor Nelson Rockefeller of New York, Richard Sichel of the Linnaean Society of New York, Jerry Sonosky of Washington, D.C., Colin Thomas of Ruxton, Maryland, Richard Wiebe of Albany, New York, and Larry Zuckerman of Brooklyn, New York.

And, finally, the author wants to acknowledge the contributions of Mrs. Ellen Strout of Milbridge, Maine, who typed the manuscript, and Ada, the author's wife, who read indefatigably, suggested material wisely, and criticized discreetly.

DISASTER BY DEFAULT:
Politics and Water Pollution

One: The Malignant Flood

In the spring of 1965 the Secretary of Health, Education and Welfare called a conference at Chicago to investigate the "gross pollution" of that area of Lake Michigan from which five million Chicagoans and suburbanites take their drinking water. A government report charged 35 municipalities and 40 industries with having caused "significant damage" to the lake. Bitter exchanges flared between public health officials and spokesmen for local industry. Among the industries under attack was the Youngstown Sheet and Tube Company, which was represented at the conference by A. J. Cochrane, assistant to the operating vice-president of the company's plant at nearby East Chicago, Indiana. While explaining what the plant was doing to treat its oil-heavy wastes, Cochrane said that equipment had been installed to "take care of one-half our present oil waste load in the plant."

"What happens to the other half of the oil waste load?"

Clarence Klassen of the Illinois Sanitary Water Board asked.

"The other half we are still working on," Cochrane said.

"When can we expect it to be corrected?" Klassen, wary of possible industry delays, persisted.

"We are working with our state officials on that at the present time," Cochrane said. "We will expect to work this problem out with them in the future."

"In other words," Klassen said, "that's the answer to 'when?' To me, that isn't satisfactory, but if this is what you want in the record—"

A report submitted by Mr. Cochrane shrugged off the lake's pollution on the grounds that Chicago's drinking water is "safe."

"The reason that the Chicago water is safe," Klassen told him, "is because of the competency in the operation of the Chicago water supply, not because of the contributions made by your company."

Here Frank Chesrow, Chicago's Health Commissioner, interrupted. "Yes," he said, "Chicago does have safe drinking water, but at a price."

"I quite agree with you on that point," Cochrane nodded. "It is at a price, yes, and a heavy price."

At a heavy price and, he might have added, at a considerable risk. As in many other cities throughout America, there is only the uncertain barrier of overburdened purification plants between Chicago's people and a flow of foul-tasting, possibly disease-infested water. A temporary failure by men or machinery, and that water will be in the taps of a million homes.

"People are afraid to talk about water pollution today,

just as they were afraid to talk about TB many years ago," a United States Public Health Service official said recently. But it is becoming increasingly difficult to ignore the quality of the water around us. We live amid sewers, whatever their labels. Here is a description, contained in a government report, of the Illinois Waterway which flows through the heart of Chicago: "Visual aesthetic nuisances, most of which have been observed occasionally and others frequently throughout the waterway are condoms, feces, grease and heavy oil, oil slicks, detergent foam, a few dying and many dead fish, gas bubbles from sludge deposits, in some areas giving the appearance of a heavy shower on the water, sludge clumps rising to the surface, paper products, discarded lumber, trees and tree limbs, metal cans, unidentified debris and a gray to dark color of water." The report goes on to describe a number of "septic odors" arising from the water. The Illinois Waterway apparently lacks only one element, for the report mentions "a very nearly total absence of bottom organisms with the exception of sludge worms."

Chicago's plight is not unique. A Washington *Post* editorial at the end of 1964 deplored the steady flow of sewage from our capital into the Potomac River because of obsolete treatment plants. "The odor is objectionable," the *Post* said of the Potomac. "The equivalent of the full sewage of a city one-fourth our size is being pumped back into the river." New York City pours a half-billion gallons of inadequately treated sewage into its rivers and harbor each day; only 35 of the city's 575 miles of coastline are safe for swimming. The Delaware River, which flows through Philadelphia and Camden, is "perhaps one of the most horribly polluted situations that we find in this country today," according to Congressman John Dingell of Michigan, who has sponsored anti-pollution measures in Congress.

Raw sewage from domestic kitchens and toilets began to turn most of our loveliest rivers into open sewers late in the 19th century. Bacteria generally associated with human wastes proliferated. People sickened and died. The vast flow of the rivers and, later, the construction of rudimentary water-purification and sewage-treatment plants, was believed to be all that was necessary to counteract the menace of our cities' noxious effluent. Only a dozen years ago a sanitary engineer could write with apparent confidence that "our polluted streams flow through healthy communities." His thesis was that the science of water purification had kept pace with the increasing pollutional load of the streams. No one can speak with such confidence today. The ugly pallor of disease is glimpsed here and there through what engineers call "the cosmetic treatment" of our waterways. Since 1945 there have been more than 30 epidemics, affecting from six to 20,000 persons, attributed in different parts of the world to waterborne infectious hepatitis. Occasionally typhoid fever is reported in this country and traced to drinking water. The polio virus has been detected in municipal water supplies. "A few years ago the only water-borne virus diseases were hepatitis and poliomyelitis," says Harry P. Kramer, Director of the Taft Sanitary Engineering Center in Cincinnati. "Today there are over one hundred." An outbreak of encephalitis in New Jersey during 1964, which killed eight people, was indirectly attributed to water pollution; the state's Commissioner of Health, calling the outbreak "a disgrace for the state," said badly polluted streams had provided extensive breeding grounds for mosquitoes, which carry the disease.

To the wastes of a growing population have been added the wastes of the world's greatest industrial and agricultural power; today our waterways are overwhelmed by offal, pesticides, acid mine drainage, wood fibers, detergent wastes, and a torrent of chemicals which are not only destructive in themselves but which combine in water to form new chemicals whose effects on human beings are not even known. Every day the city of Omaha dumps 300,000 pounds of paunch manure, the partially digested hay and corn removed from the stomachs of slaughtered cattle, into the Missouri River. The salinity of the Colorado River has been so intensified by the minerals it picks up while irrigating the fields of southwestern farmers that the Mexican government complained bitterly to Washington. Sometimes the water which crosses the border has ruined the wheat and cotton crops of farmers in the Mexicali Valley. James M. Quigley, an Assistant Secretary of Health, Education and Welfare who investigated the 1964 Mississippi fish kill (blamed on the pesticide Endrin) told a Senate committee that if he were in New Orleans he would not care to eat a Gulf shrimp cocktail. The quality of Maine's Androscoggin River, polluted chiefly by pulp wastes from paper mills, was described by a Public Health Service report (in what homeowners along its shores could scarcely interpret as reassuring words) to be "at a level that will just prevent the development of obnoxious conditions."

The old adage that in water "there is dilution of pollution" is obsolete. Rivers which once were able to break down the wastes poured into them are now overloaded.

The great mass of wastes and the new persistent chemicals are carried farther by water than ever before, so that a river flowing past one town sweeps its pollution downstream to the next town—and often into the next state. "It shocks and revolts me," Connecticut's Senator Abraham Ribicoff said in 1964, "to learn that where the Connecticut River crosses the state line from Massachusetts the water is so foul that a single drop has a bacteria count 315 times greater than the bacteriological standard used by Connecticut in approving bathing sites on the river."

Despite the frightening composition of 20th-century wastes, both local government and industrial leaders continue to look on rivers primarily as sewers. Most cities do not wallow in their own filth, but pump it into the river at a point where it has already flowed past heavily populated areas. Their wastes are carried away and inflicted on their neighbors downstream. It is difficult to persuade local voters to supply the necessary funds for sewage-treatment plants when it is generally the downstream cities that will benefit from the appropriation. Vast national waterways are polluted because citizens and local governments have shrugged off their responsibility.

"Sometimes a problem reaches Washington because of local default," a *New York Times* editorial recently said. "Water pollution would not have become a federal responsibility if so many state and local governments had not been negligent in protecting their rivers."

When the federal government, through the Department of Health, Education and Welfare, has stepped in to investigate a particularly dangerous local pollution source, it has too often been frustrated by resentful officials of the municipal and state governments. It is then that the cry of "States Rights" is raised. Though states rights is a complex issue, it was popularized and propagandized during the early 19th century by defenders of slavery. It has been raised in this century by racists who would deprive others of their constitutional rights and, again, by the polluters of our water and air who feel that the state is easier to deal with than a powerful and disinterested federal government.

One of Henrik Ibsen's most famous plays, *An Enemy of the People,* describes the uproar which occurs in a Norwegian resort when a local doctor discovers that the baths on which the town's prosperity is based have been polluted by industrial wastes. Prominent citizens plead with the doctor to withhold his findings. "You are trying to stop up the source of our town's prosperity," he is told. "That source is poisoned," the doctor replies. When he persists in his report, he is branded "An Enemy of the People."

This tragedy is repeated over and over throughout the United States, particularly where one industry has come to dominate an area. Any attempt to clear up outrageous sources of pollution is declared by some local politicians and businessmen, even in cases where the public health is jeopardized, to be an attempt to undercut the region's prosperity. The offending industries might move away, and jobs would be lost.

"Part of your problem, speaking very frankly," Assistant Secretary of HEW Quigley has said, "is that the polluters in a given state are likely to be your communities and your cities which belong to your political party and my political party. It gets a little embarrassing to move against your fellow partisans and embarrass them publicly or force them to float a bond issue or increase taxes.

"Secondly, in many instances your big polluters are your big employers, big industries. And at a time when the states are involved, as they have been and will continue to be, in very keen competition for industry, for jobs, it is certainly an extremely difficult job for a state governor or a state legislature to face up to some of the biggest employers in the state and say 'you must do this.'"

One of the most outspoken congressional critics of lax enforcement measures is Senator Edmund Muskie of Maine. "We haven't lost any industry in Maine because we enforced anti-pollution laws there, but we may have scared away new industries because of our dirty rivers," Muskie said recently. "Industry's protests certainly have had one effect, though. They have slowed down the pace of enforcement legislation."

The practical old-fashioned device of buying the votes of state legislators and local politicians has recently been subverted to the equally effective public relations approach. No one is as likely to wrap himself quite as firmly in the American flag as a businessman who feels that his freedom of action may be at stake. Here is an excerpt from a speech made a few years ago by Robert G. Dunlop, president of the Sun Oil Company.

"While we seek to protect our valuable water resources," Dunlop said, "let us not wear blindfolds of cynicism. I would remind you that we have in America another precious heritage—the climate of individual freedom that has encouraged the development of initiative and resourcefulness. This is the key that has unlocked the door to our Nation's treasure chest of natural resources and made them available for the benefit of our citizens."

Such sentiments would have been warmly applauded by those earlier holders of the key to "our Nation's treasure chest," who looted our forests, despoiled our plains and slaughtered our buffalo and shorebirds before Theodore Roosevelt restrained them.

Industry has vigorously fought efforts by the federal government to enforce pollution laws. During the proceedings of the National Conference on Water Pollution in 1960, Leonard E. Pasek of Kimberly-Clark Corporation argued against federal action in these words: "Historians have noted that over the centuries, Oriental despotism has been associated with centralized control of water resources."

Industry people continue to battle federal regulation with this kind of drivel. If their invocation of "free enterprise" is submerged in noxious odors rising from the stream they have just polluted, they turn to other defenses. One such defense is that the water, while it may look, smell, and taste awful, presents no hazard to the public health. The owner of a factory that was said to be a notorious polluter of the local river, and therefore a menace, tried to refute these charges recently by resort to a primitive "ordeal by poison." Before a cluster of witnesses he cheerfully swilled samples of river water collected near his factory. One cynic could not help but recall an old movie in which a lawyer stood before the jury in a murder case and tossed down a concoction said to have been fed by his client to the deceased. The jury promptly returned a verdict of acquittal. Subsequent scenes showed the lawyer plodding grimly to the courthouse door, where his aides propped up his collapsing body, put him into a car, and rushed him to a sinister-looking physician, who waited with the poison's only known antidote. One wonders.

The threat to the public health from polluted waters is

very real. During heavy rains, most municipal sewage treatment plants are overwhelmed by a flood of stormwater. At these times, sewage and stormwater alike are passed untreated to the waterways, forming bacterial "islands" off our beaches and polluting our shellfish beds. The ten thousand new chemicals developed each year create a separate menace. "Our streams have become giant test tubes for what is taking place," Mark D. Hollis of the Public Health Service has said. "Chemicals react on one another. Two parts per million of copper will not hurt fish, nor eight parts of zinc. But if you combine as little as one-tenth of those amounts of copper and zinc you will kill all the fish in the stream."

Pushed to the limit, many industrial people plead poverty. Few admit that a sewage-treatment plant is a part of their production needs. In a handful of cases the installation of a waste-treatment plant may be uneconomical; a two-line pea cannery, for instance, processing 4,000 cases a day, produces wastes equal to those of a community of 10,000 people. But the cannery operates only during the growing season—about two months a year—and treatment plants are expensive. Sometimes this inability to clean up one's own mess jeopardizes other industries as well. In 1964 Louisiana's Little River was said to be unsuitable for use to any industry because of brine which had seeped into the river from abandoned oil fields. When the Louisiana Stream Control Commission asked operators to reinject the salt water into the rock formations, the operators replied that the project was too costly. A whole region suffered.

Earle G. Hubbard, a North Carolina expert, is among those, however, who has challenged industry's plea that it cannot afford proper sewage treatment. "The lack, or so-called lack, of financial capability is not the real reason," he has said. "I think the lack of awareness of the need of it and the lack of desire to capitalize necessary treatment are still perhaps major factors in our failure to move forward with waste treatment as rapidly as we need."

Many industries have resisted state and federal attempts to get them to build treatment facilities. Others have hampered government efforts to investigate their current wastes. A great deal of research is needed to determine exactly what substances are poured into our waterways, and what measures must be taken to neutralize them. Certain industries object to these disclosures on the grounds that the makeup of their products would inevitably be exposed to their competitors (this objection is nonsense; one way or another, most industries exchange "trade secrets" with their rivals in the same way that others conspire together to fix prices). In any case, Senator Muskie prefers to take a strong line with quibblers. "If these industries would rather have the government establish policy *without* the facts, then it's their decision," he says.

In other industries there is an ambivalent attitude toward conservation. One division of Olin-Mathieson, for instance, manufactures firearms for hunters, and is therefore solidly behind the conservation of natural resources. Another division of Olin-Mathieson manufactures chemicals, which in the past have contributed pollution to nearby rivers. The public relations arm of a major meatpacking firm was chagrined during a "goodwill" campaign several years ago to discover that its own company antagonized people along the Missouri River by polluting it with the remnants of slaughtered animals.

There is an overt sense of frustration among concerned

legislators and officials. Questioning a representative of the pulp industry before his House sub-committee some time ago, Congressman Robert E. Jones of Alabama wondered why the paper companies could not control their wastes.

"It is economics that is really holding us back," he was told.

"The economics of the company?" Jones asked.

"To the industry," the paper executive said.

"To the industry? Well, they are doing pretty well, aren't they?" Jones persisted.

"They seem to be in a favorable position in the world market," the executive said.

"Then why can't they do that? I mean, after all, they are taking water out of the public streams. They are operating in the public domain. Why can't they manage that? We are building dams; we are building navigation projects. I don't know of anyone that has been more sympathetic to the paper companies than the Congress of the United States. Why can't they recognize our problem?"

Jones' frustration has been echoed by concerned politicians and conservationists all over the United States. To many people a river's prime use is as a source of drinking water; it is a source of life, both for human beings and for fish and other wildlife. Industrialists, on the other hand, consider a river's primary function to be sewage disposal. Rivers, like other portions of our national heritage, have been appropriated by industry as business assets. Their use by human beings and wildlife has become a secondary concern, which, in many of our most badly polluted rivers, means that there is *no* secondary concern. Is it naïve to want it otherwise? Too often the so-called "aesthetic" considerations are placed at the bottom of the list when one is advancing reasons why some particularly outrageous rape of our natural resources should be restricted. As if human beings must apologize for an instinct that helps to distinguish us from the brutes!

The question the American people must answer is this: is a polluted river well used? Many of our rivers, despite years of efforts to clean them up, remain sewers—biological deserts unfit for drinking, fishing, swimming, or even for boating. In 1960 Dr. Leroy E. Burney, Surgeon General under President Eisenhower, summed up our water problem this way: "The condition of our waters is a national disgrace. It is tragic for the world's richest, most powerful and most technologically advanced nation to foul its own nest, limit its growth and threaten the health of its people."

In the years since then we have spent millions of dollars on waste-treatment facilities, and yet the problem remains the same. That region is fortunate whose waters have not been further degraded. In the past only a great disaster like the Crash of 1929, the Mississippi flood of 1937, or the ravages in the "Dust Bowl" have been able to jar Americans from their complacency. The story of the pollution of our waterways suggests that the American people may be drifting toward another shock.

Two: The Stage Is Set

I

In his book *Medieval Panorama,* the English historian G. G. Coulton described 14th-century Cambridge: "Very common presentments are those which testify to terrible disorder and filth in the streets—dung heaps are as ubiquitous here as at Bury St. Edmunds, though a great advance was made in 1401 by the enactment that such heaps should be cleared every week . . . Swine ran about the streets and rooted amid its garbage . . . and, worst of all, 'certain noxious open gutters made by the Masters of Michaelhouse and Gonville Hall, which ran from those colleges to the High Street, through which many masters and scholars had access to the schools of the University, gave out an abominable stench, and so corrupted the air that many masters and scholars passing fell sick thereof;' quite apart, we may suppose, from their noxious effects on the actual inmates of Michaelhouse and Gonville Hall."

The modern man, who washes daily, equips his home with the newest sanitary devices, pours his garbage into metal cans or incinerators, and flushes his other wastes out through a pipe, is appalled by a description of garbage-infested medieval cities. He considers himself a level above the barbarians who did not flush away their wastes, but lived among them. Yet, in a very real sense, modern man's plight and environment are the same. His wastes do not evaporate any more readily than did those of the medieval townsman. They simply are conveyed by pipes into the nearest waterway, and the rivers which flow through and around his city are as garbage-laden as the muddy, epidemic-breeding streets of his ancestors.

Until the 20th century, man had not progressed beyond the public health practices of ancient Rome and, indeed, in most cases, had fallen far behind it. The grandeur that was Rome included aqueducts and sewers, as well as coliseums and temples. (In sanitary practices, as well as in other matters, the Romans were seldom innovators: the ancient Chinese are said to have used artificial means of settling the solids out of their drinking water, while the Bible's Pool of Siloam was a cesspool.) But the Romans worked on a monumental scale. Aqueducts, constructed of stone and lined with cement, brought 38 million gallons of water each day to their city. Lead pipes channelled the water from them into fountains, baths, shops, and even into the homes of the wealthy. Sewers carried off waste waters. The greatest of these was the Cloaca Maxima, lined with concrete, bricks, and tile and so large that it was said a loaded wagon could be driven through its massive stone arches. Through holes in the streets waste and rain water ran into the sewers and finally into the Tiber, to mingle perhaps with the remains of noble Romans tossed there by their political enemies. And so the Tiber was the first of the western world's famous rivers to become a sewer.

As the world fell apart under the barbarian onslaught, so, too, did man's ideas of sanitation. Feudal society was not congested, and waste was not a problem. It was only with the rise of cities that people began again to cluster about filth. Though the belief was widely held during the Middle Ages that small insects, worms, and "animalculae" were generated spontaneously from putrefaction, the people treated their wastes casually. Rain water ran in currents along the curbs of the larger cities, and residents of the bordering houses yielded to the same temptation that our own society does when it sees flowing water: they poured their wastes into it.

There were early attempts at regulation. Venice, in the 14th century, established a municipal board of health, and followed Marseilles' lead in requiring plague-infested ships to remain at a distant harbor anchorage for 40 days before docking (and from those 40 days comes our word "quarantine"). London, in the same century, tried to discourage its citizens from emptying their tubs and chamber pots out windows into the streets below, but without much success. Apparently it was safer to walk the streets of Paris, for there the considerate citizens preceded the shower with the warning cry, "Gar l'eau!"

But European civilization survived, and some of its representatives eventually settled the New World. Here the pattern was repeated. Early colonial America was sparsely settled. Towns were widely spaced, and the relatively small quantities of wastes emptied into nearby rivers were well diluted when they reached the next settlement downstream. But by the end of the 18th century, only a few years after the nation's birth, epidemics began to ravage the larger cities of the East Coast. The people of New York dumped "tubbs of nastiness" into the streets. Dead dogs and cats were tossed into ponds from which people drew their drinking water. Robert Daley, in *The World Beneath the City,* quotes an early 19th century description of a pond which was a major source of the city's drinking water: ". . . a shocking hole where all impure things center together and engender the worst of unwholesome productions; foul with excrement, frogspawn and reptiles . . . Can you bear to drink it on Sundays in the summertime? It is so bad before Monday morning as to be very sickly and nauseating. Plague will make a yearly slaughter until you furnish better water."

Well-to-do citizens and most horses refused to drink New York water, the well-to-do buying it from remote private supplies and the horses doing the best they could. The poor were stuck with it, and epidemics broke out in the slums. As is customary in a period of public disaster, there were private interests ready to step in and take their profit. Aaron Burr and his associates founded the Manhattan Company, which was given permission by the New York State Legislature to supply water to the City of New York. The Manhattan Company's directors, however, cultivated a larger ambition. Along with the rights to bring water to the city, the directors sought and got a charter to establish a bank, to be called the Bank of the Manhattan Company. From the profits expected to be earned from the banking business, Burr hoped to finance a campaign for the Presidency of the United States. There was a great deal of maneuvering, mostly behind the scenes. Describing the affair in *Water For the Cities,* Nelson M. Blake has written: "The conflict of interest revealed here borders on the fantastic . . . DeWitt Clinton participated on one side as mayor of the city and on the other as the most active director of the company. But this was not the full extent of Clinton's involvement. He was also a senator from the southern district and thus a powerful figure in the legislature, which had the power to grant the needed authority to the city and the company. Finally, be it noted, that the Bank of the Manhattan Company held DeWitt Clinton's notes for at least $8,900."

Burr's political fortunes waned after his fatal duel with Alexander Hamilton and the company's inept schemes to bring water (inadequate in both quantity and quality) to New York finally subsided in the face of public indignation. But the bank prospered. It stands today as the Chase Manhattan Bank, one of the pillars of Wall Street.

New York's water problem persisted, too, and there were less ambitious attempts to find a drinking supply. One prominent tanner sank a deep well, which produced a singularly foul-tasting drink. Undaunted, he convinced the local people that anything so unappetizing must possess therapeutic value. He did a thriving business in "medicinal water" until it was discovered that the source of his well was contaminated by old tannery wastes. Fortunately, nobody died. In fact, certain forms of pollution received a kind of official sanction. An 1831 report from the New York Lyceum of Natural History claimed that the element which kept the city well water from being even more contaminated than it happened to be was the urine which seeped into it from nearby privies.

"This liquid, when stale or putrid," said the report, "has the remarkable property of precipitating the earthy salts from their solution, or in other words, it makes hard waters soft. Although the fastidious may revolt from the use of water thus sweetened to our palate, it is perhaps fortunate that this mixture is daily taking place, for otherwise the water of this city would become in a much shorter space of time than it actually does, utterly unfit for domestic purposes."

New York's water supply, inadequate and badly contaminated, remained a national disgrace until the middle of the 19th century. Then the great aqueduct bringing water from the Croton north of New York was completed by the city itself. After years of disastrous plagues and fires, and intolerable bickering among politicians, one resident can be forgiven for noting, as fountains sprayed and people bathed, "Political spouting has given way to water spouts."

But even those cities which were beginning to solve (temporarily, at least) their drinking-water problems were still faced with alarming problems of waste disposal. What naturalist Marston Bates calls man's "present cancer-like spree of reproduction" had already begun. Filth was stockpiled in congested cities, especially in those areas inhabited by the poor. There was increased speculation about the market value of human wastes: 19th century scientists computed that the excretion of one man during the year was sufficient to fertilize about 800 pounds of grain.

Fortunately, the notion was spreading that filth was somehow associated with the devastating plagues of cholera and yellow fever which continued through the century. Cities struggled, if mostly ineffectually, to clean themselves up. Philadelphia, for instance, passed an ordinance which imposed a fine of five dollars on anyone who bathed in, excreted in, or tossed dead animals into a source of the the local water supply. To demonstrate their good faith, the city fathers offered to pay half of a collected fine to the informer.

In the middle of the 19th century there occurred several landmarks in the struggle against water-borne disease. Another in a series of decimating cholera epidemics swept London in 1854. Dr. John Snow, Queen Victoria's physician, noticed that the epidemic was concentrated in a poorer section of the city, around the public water pump which stood on Broad Street. Reasoning that perhaps seepage from nearby privies had contaminated the well there, he demanded the removal of the pump's handle. When the handle was removed, the epidemic subsided.

Such circumstantial evidence was soon confirmed by 19th-century science. The development of effective microscopes led to Pasteur's "germ" theory in the 1870's. Until this time it had been almost universally believed that water which did not offend the senses was above suspicion. Now the microscope revealed the presence of all sorts of "animalculae" in water, and scientists were able eventually to isolate and identify the harmful ones. But this theory came as quite a shock. A cartoon, drawn shortly after the discovery of tiny organisms in Boston's drinking water, depicted an old Irishman peering into a microscope.

"Well, did anybody ever see the likes of this!" he was exclaiming to a crowd around him. "They call whiskey 'a droph o' the creature.' But here's water that's a droph of a thousand creatures!"

The discovery was as upsetting to many people as it would be to us if we learned that we were eating maggots in our meat. There was a general outcry now to channel wastes away from vital ponds and wells, and into the nearest rivers, where they presumably would be carried safely away. Sewage construction was still primitive. In many cases, it consisted simply of a cover over whatever natural flow of water passed through the center of town. Later, large troughs of brick and stone were built and covered, and into these were conveyed or thrown the city's wastes. Street runoff, particularly filthy because of horse droppings and the casual accumulation there of garbage, made up a great part of this "sewage." Demands for more systematic sewer construction generally met with apathy among civic leaders. One of America's most prominent sanitary engineers during the 19th century, Colonel George E. Waring, Jr., once commented on a situation which transcended his time. "Communities are slow to try experiments in engineering," Waring said, "and the force of precedent has such effect nowhere else as with the class of minds usually charged with the regulation of municipal affairs."

In looking back at the water pollution problems of a hundred years ago, one constantly encounters situations and comments which ring with irony today. Not the least of these ironies is that our ancestors also recognized the enormity of the stormwater problem. Authors of modern reports seem to be saying something new when they advocate the separation of our sewers to provide one set for domestic and industrial wastes, and another for stormwater runoff. Yet in 1842, Edwin Chadwick, who was called "the father of sanitation in England," urged the separation of sewers. "Household wastes and matters of like character should be provided for by a separate and distinct system of pipes," he said. A modern public health officer could not be more explicit.

Apparently nobody listened, for 40 years later our own Colonel Waring was saying the same thing. In 1881 he wrote a pamphlet in which he said that the problem of stormwater "is the most pressing one in sewerage engineering at this time . . . simplicity, economy, and above all, the best observance of sanitary requirements demand in almost all cases, if not indeed everywhere, an absolute separation of household and manufacturing waste from the surface flow."

Another irony is that the city of Memphis, which was to be the center of a great public health controversy in our own time, was among the first American cities to install an "admirable" sewer system. Like most other changes in our country, this was motivated by disaster. In 1878, yellow fever struck the city, leaving 5,000 people dead between August 14 and November 3. When another epidemic broke out in Memphis the following year, the city fathers ordered a survey of its sanitary conditions. One observer's description will suffice here. "The whole city," he said, "under as well as upon the surface, was reeking with organic filth." The man chosen to give Memphis its first sewer system was Colonel Waring. Here he put into practice his notions of a separate sewer system for domestic use. Four-inch pipes were laid from each house into the streets, where they fed into six-inch pipes and then into trunk sewers. The latter finally emptied into Wolf River.

It might have been a model sewer system except for the fact that the city ran out of money and laid the pipes without providing access to them from manholes in the streets. This caused many disturbances. Bottles, fragments of bricks, and other heavy objects became stuck in the pipes ("frequent in the lower class neighborhoods and in the vicinity of public schools") and workers were forever digging up the city streets. But, on the whole, the sewer system was judged to be a splendid engineering feat and Memphis became a more healthy place in which to live. Several years later Waring was able to write, with understandable pride, that Memphis "has accepted advice more radical, probably, than was ever seriously given before, has raised the money for the required work, and has put its house into more nearly perfect order than has any other town in the country."

Few other cities deserved any praise. Despite its new aqueduct, growing New York suffered from a lack of drinking water and a surplus of sewage. An editorial in the New York *Herald* on November 23, 1875, said that "we drink malarious water cooled with malarious ice, and live and sleep in an atmosphere stifling with sewer gas." There was a notion that the horrible stench rising from New York sewers could be dissipated by pouring buckets of perfume into them. Other, wiser, men saw that the solution must be far more thorough, that there had to be a concept of "public health" planted among the more influential people in American cities. Deploring New York's death rate, which was 20 percent higher than that of either London or Paris, a prominent engineer named Charles Haswell wrote in 1875: "The functions of a board of health should not be restricted to giving permits for burial and registering deaths; they should extend to the institution and requirements of such means as would lessen both the occurrence of the one and the necessity of the other."

The country at last appeared to be groping in the right direction.

II

Before the science of bacteriology revolutionized medicine near the close of the 19th century, most public health action was intermittent and feeble. It arose, and subsided, with an emergency. The public proceeded to bury its dead. The management of a city's water supply and waste disposal projects was considered to be a job for engineers and businessmen. There were primitive boards of health in many seaport towns early in the century, but their functions were restricted to matters of quarantine: as "ports of entry" into the United States, these coastal cities were the first and often the hardest hit by plagues imported from abroad. But for the most part quarantine, like all other public health projects, was a "police" action. Temporary boards sometimes assisted the police. By mid-century, municipal boards of health were still an emergency device or, even worse, simply a political plaything to which party hacks were appointed. There was no public health legislation.

In 1853 the local boards of health dealing with quarantine in Louisiana proved so ineffectual that a state board, the nation's first, was set up. It assumed all quarantine duties. After the Civil War, most states set up similar boards, and quarantine became a province of the states. In nearly every case the state boards were starved for funds and proper staffs (and sometimes even for a full-time director).

State boards proved nearly as inadequate as their municipal counterparts in stemming the frightening wave of plagues from abroad. It soon became evident that only the federal government was able to police the nation's ports effectively. In less than a hundred years our "stage-coach civilization" had been completely transformed by the Industrial Revolution and the miracles of the new sciences. Designed to remedy many of the flaws in the Articles of Confederation, the Constitution of 1789 declared that the federal government must have control over trade and other vital matters between the states. The states managed to keep for themselves all those powers not specifically mentioned in the Constitution. The framers of the Constitution had not foreseen the incredibly complex problems in public health which the next century would create. As Robert D. Leigh, Professor of Government at Williams College, wrote in 1927, "An arrangement of governmental powers made for a town-pump and pest-house world has become the instrument of determining governmental powers in an era of international sanitation."

In the face of states' rights resistance, the federal government was often powerless to intervene in any cases affecting the public health. Only an amendment to the Constitution would have given the government precedence in many cases and, as Professor Leigh has pointed out, the only amendment ever passed which might be construed as pertaining to the public health was the 18th, or Prohibition, Amendment. A struggle over national quarantine raged throughout most of the 19th century. Though the nation suffered from successive waves of epidemics (yellow fever, Asiatic cholera, bubonic plague), states'-righters apparently lived more in dread of their government. Enraged by this idiocy, Senator Edmunds took the Senate floor in 1866 to plead for federal supervision of quarantine. "Cholera," he said, "will not pay any attention to state lines. It does not know anything about state rights."

Finally, in 1878, a National Quarantine Act was passed by Congress. The Surgeon General was given certain powers in dealing with vessels carrying disease, and the United States Marine Hospital Service (which eventually was to become the Public Health Service) took over some of the duties formerly handled by the states. Little by little the quarantine laws in this country were strengthened. Too often, however, the federal government had to overcome bitter state opposition to do its job. Officials in Mississippi and Louisiana constantly hampered federal quarantine officers in the latter half of the 19th century and only in 1905, during the last great outbreak of yellow fever there, did New Orleans call for assistance from the government.

The National Quarantine Act, like almost all other legislation dealing with the public health, was enacted under the federal government's uncontested right to supervise matters of foreign and interstate commerce (as spelled out under the Constitution's "commerce clause"). When the appearance at markets of rotten meat imperiled the public health, for instance, the government was able to intervene only by prohibiting the shipment of diseased livestock in interstate commerce (which it did in 1884, later extending the prohibition to include livestock exposed to disease, as well).

Meanwhile, most cities had, by the end of the 19th century, taken steps to protect their water supplies. Those cities on rivers which carried down to them the pollutants of their neighbors upstream constructed plants to filter and otherwise purify their drinking water. The new science of bacteriology had proven that dangers lurked in the lakes and rivers of modern civilization. Cholera, for instance, was found to be contracted from water polluted by organisms contained in the excreta of cholera victims. Slow sand filters (purifying about two million gallons of water per acre each day) had been used in England for years; Parliament in 1852 made it compulsory to filter all river water used by London.

In 1892 cities which had been slow to build purification plants were shocked into action by the cholera epidemic which killed 8,600 people at Hamburg, Germany. Human wastes discharged from ships anchored in the Elbe River sowed and nourished the epidemic. Altona, a neighboring city which took its water from the same river but filtered it before releasing it as potable (Hamburg did not), escaped almost entirely. Only 39 people died in Altona, all of whom were proved either to have been in contact with diseased persons or to have drunk Hamburg water. The people of American cities were justly frightened. Typhoid plagues ravaged Lawrence, Lowell, and other Massachusetts cities on the polluted Merrimack River at the end of the 19th century. The death rate in Lawrence from typhoid was 134 per 100,000 people in 1894, and seldom went much lower during those years.

American cities now turned increasingly to science and technology in their efforts to cut into the outrageous death rates. Filtration and, later, chlorination and other modern methods were used to destroy the harmful bacteria consigned them by cities upstream. The ingenuity Americans began to display in contaminating and then purifying their drinking water sometimes approached the dream logic of Alice's White Knight, who had a plan to dye his whiskers green,

> And always use so large a fan
> That they could not be seen.

But American ingenuity has been uniquely destructive as well as inventive. No nation on earth has ever destroyed its natural resources with the speed and thoroughness with which Americans of the 19th century went about it. Under the banner of "free enterprise," economic pirates plundered our forests, wasted our topsoil, and contaminated our rivers. Devastation was justified by what Rachel Carson was to call "the false assurances that whatever is financially profitable is good for the nation and for mankind."

If the onslaught was somewhat abated at the beginning of the 20th century, the greatest share of the credit must go to Theodore Roosevelt and the band of dedicated men who were attracted to him and his views. Perhaps the foremost conservationist in Roosevelt's administration was Gifford Pinchot, who once described forestry as "the art of using the forest without destroying it." It was Roosevelt's desire to apply similar standards to all of our resources before they were totally destroyed. Until his administration, the single law which Congress had passed dealing with the pollution of our waters was the Rivers and Harbors Act of 1899. One section of this act prohibited the discharge into navigable waters of masses of sewage sufficient to impede navigation. If the cause of navigation was served, that of public health was not: a river can absorb a rather ample load of pollution before it is decided that ships cannot plow through it.

The Inland Waterways Commission, appointed by Roosevelt in 1908, issued a report which said in part: "We recommend that hereafter any plans for the use of inland waterways in connection with interstate commerce shall regard the streams of the country as an asset of the people, shall take full account of the conservation of all resources connected with running waters and shall look to the protection of those resources from monopoly and to their administration in the interests of the people."

It stated the issue, but there was little legislation at the time to alter the condition it deplored. There was, among other assaults, a concerted attempt by private power interests to seize the rivers for their own designs. The position of these people was spelled out in 1908 by Captain William Patrick Lay, president of the Alabama Power Company. "The water powers, their undeveloped state along the rivers of this country," Lay said, "belong to riparian owners, under the sovereignty of the states, subject, of course, to the prior rights of navigation and navigation only. This is a property right, the protection of which is guaranteed by the constitution of the United States and those of the several states."

Lay went on to attack "self-styled conservationists" and "would-be bureaucrats," having wrapped himself securely in the Constitution, which apparel seems to take the place of a mask and burglar tools for those who plunder the public on a large scale. During a White House "Conference of Governors on Conservation" the same year, Alabama's Governor Braxton Bragg Comer came to the defense of the private power interests. Those interests wanted to appropriate Muscle Shoals on the Tennessee River (now a part of TVA) for themselves. "We believe it will be dangerous to tinker with the sacred rights of state sovereignty," said Comer, who feared interference by the federal government.

"We are greatly indebted to Governor Comer for his speech against centralization," President Roosevelt replied. "Governor, I do not understand that you object to the national government appropriating money to clear out Muscle Shoals?"

There was laughter and applause from the audience. The governor was silent.

The rising clamor for some kind of federal supervision in public health produced the Public Health Service Act of 1912. In his last message to Congress in December, 1908, Roosevelt had recommended the establishment of a national health board. Despite bitter opposition from a number of organized groups (among them the hydropaths, chiropractors, Christian Scientists, the Anti-Vivisection League, and various patent-medicine manufacturers), the Act of 1912 created the United States Public Health Service much as we know it today. The act authorized the investigation of water pollution where it affected man's health, but provided meager enforcement procedures. Only in those areas dealing with interstate transportation was the Public Health Service able to move effectively. Here the PHS insisted that the railroads provide clean drinking water, and that the common towel and common drinking cup be abolished. Widely-divergent water quality standards across the country had made a mockery of previous attempts to insure a supply of good drinking water aboard trains; the supplies in some localities were actually contaminated. The PHS established a set of standards for purity, a project it later turned back to the states while retaining the right to advise.

Without an enforcement arm in other areas, the federal government was unable to reverse the rapid deterioration of the nation's waterways after World War I. A reaction to the centralization of government (stimulated in part by the excesses of that war's bloated amateur bureaucracy), a keen resentment of Prohibition and a general swing to the Right in politics, killed every impulse toward anti-pollution legislation in Congress. Only the Oil Pollution Act of 1924, controlling oil discharges in coastal waters damaging to aquatic life, harbors, docks, and recreational facilities, brightened a dismal congressional record. When the Izaak Walton League was asked by President Coolidge's administration to survey pollution in our inland waters, it released in 1927 a shocking report. "A civilized community is morally bound to take care of its wastes in a decent and sanitary manner," the report said, "and not throw its filth out the back door to incubate and spread disease." The report documented the fact that Americans had done just that. Sewage treatment had lagged because of the early success in purifying drinking water. Now more than 85 percent of America's inland waterways were polluted and only 30 percent of its population lived in communities which treated their wastes. Of that 30 percent, many were served by inadequate facilities.

Water pollution soon proved a financial burden to the public as well as a menace to its health. In 1929, Olean, New York (with a population of 22,000), was obliged to float a bond issue totaling $350,000 to pay the damages awarded by the courts to people who had contracted typhoid fever after drinking the city's water. Modern treatment facilities strained under the burden of purifying water which carried heavier loads of pollution each year. America had passed from the "Microbiological Era" to the "Microchemical Era." Our cities had become islands surrounded and infiltrated by open sewers nourishing the foulest human and industrial wastes.

Curiously, during the 1930's this nation seemed about to come to grips with the problem. The massive public works program under the New Deal included the construction of municipal sewage plants, enabling many cities to treat their wastes more effectively than at any time before or since. Title Six of the Social Security Act provided grants for local public health programs; staffs were increased, and schools of public health established.

World War II (and later the Korean War) wiped out this brave start. Money and materials were diverted to more pressing matters. The construction and renovation of treatment plants were abandoned. The chemical and heavy-metals industries produced enormous changes in the quality of our streams. "I have seen streams 'die' overnight," Senator Muskie says. "They no longer could assimilate the complex wastes we poured into them. America has never managed to correct the balance."

It was only in 1948 that Congress took its first tentative steps toward facing the problem. In the preceding 60 years there had been over 100 anti-pollution bills introduced in Congress. None had been passed, as Congress wilted before the popular front of states'-righters, free enterprisers, and other guardians of the inherent human right to destroy our God-given resources. Then, in 1948, Congress passed the first "Water Pollution Control Act."

"The 1948 act passed only because Senator Taft, the Great Conservative, got up on the Senate floor and said that in his opinion it was constitutional," an aide to another prominent senator has said. "That's what it took to pass it."

The act was merely experimental, failing to provide funds for waste treatment and incorporating a cumbersome enforcement procedure. This sketchy federal program was dumped into the lap of the Public Health Service, chiefly for want of a better place. There was not even a full-time enforcement officer assigned to the program. There was, however, a lawyer named Murray Stein attached to the PHS General Counsel. A graduate of George Washington University and one of the junior members of the staff, Stein was occasionally relieved of his other duties to look into pollution cases.

"There wasn't much to be done," Stein recalls today. He is a stocky, round-faced man with thinning dark hair and thick eyeglasses. When he refers to polluters, his face crinkles into a wry grin, much like that of a prep-school headmaster saying, "Boys will be boys, but are they going to catch hell!" He obviously regrets some missed opportunities in the old days. "It wasn't because the 1948 Act was a bad law, but nobody was really anxious to begin large-scale actions against the polluters. But I picked up some valuable experience." It was six years before Stein was able to put that experience to good use and become, as chief enforcement officer of the PHS Pollution Control Division, the mailed fist of this belated crusade.

If the war on pollution has had another hero, it is Congressman John A. Blatnik of Minnesota. Blatnik came to Washington as a young congressman from the northern rural region of his state. A former CCC worker, he had spent a great deal of time in the woods and observed the ravages inflicted on our natural resources by the greedy and the ignorant. Of the water pollution problem, Blatnik himself was blissfully unaware.

"There wasn't any such thing in my part of Minnesota," he said recently. "When I came to Washington I began to get visits from people in my district, and of course if it was spring I'd take them to the Potomac Tidal Basin to see the cherry blossoms. Sometimes they'd ask me what that funny smell was. I couldn't tell them. I was so naïve I just thought that was the way all tidal water was supposed to smell. It took me a few years to discover that the Tidal Basin near the cherry trees is the best dressed sewer in the world."

By way of his general concern for natural resources Blatnik grew interested in water pollution. He was one of the leading figures in pushing the first permanent antipollution legislation through Congress. A man close to Blatnik at the time has recalled the struggle.

"Until 1956 water pollution legislation had always been pushed strictly as a public health measure," this man said. "The people who were against the various pollution bills were able to squash them because disease was always beneath the surface. You can't get the public aroused about public health measures unless you have sick people. The same thing happened in the 1960's when Senator Kefauver was trying to push through his legislation controlling the drug industry. People were getting misled by the drug manufacturers but the drugs themselves didn't seem to have any bad effects—there were no sick people —and so the bill didn't have broad enough support. The only thing that saved the bill—God help us—was the thalidomide tragedy.

"There wasn't any big water-borne epidemic in 1956, so Blatnik found his support elsewhere. He simply put the emphasis on the destruction of our natural resources. He was always a resource man, anyway. He went to the people and said, 'Pollution will destroy your water supply just as surely as a drought will.' He changed water pollution from a health to a conservation problem. The people bought it."

In drafting the Federal Water Pollution Control Act of 1956* Blatnik and other interested legislators ran into heated opposition from industry. Industry lobbyists were disturbed by the enforcement procedure. Above all they did not want the federal government to haul an offender into court. They suggested that the first step in the enforcement procedure be a conference, open to the public, at which state officials might present their cases, and industry be invited to demonstrate what steps it had taken, and was about to take, to abate local pollution.

It is ironic that today many industrial leaders complain bitterly about the "open" conference. These conferences, presided over by Murray Stein and sanctioned by the 1956 Act in which John Blatnik played such a leading part, have dramatically revealed the nature of America's water pollution, and the identity of the polluters.

* A summary of federal water pollution legislation can be found in the appendix.

Three: Those Slaughterhouses on the Missouri

I

Armed at last with the power to confront the polluters, the United States Government cast about in 1957 for a suitable battleground. Its choice fell on the Missouri River, which was eminently qualified. Though America's longest waterway, the Missouri did not have a single city of size along its 2500-mile length which treated its sewage. On its banks stood the great meat-packing centers of America. Raw domestic wastes from Sioux City, Omaha, St. Joseph, and Kansas City, with those of dozens of lesser towns, fouled the river. Mingling with the domestic sewage were the blood, hooves, hair, and paunch manure of hundreds of thousands of slaughtered animals. This grisly flow, moving toward its junction with the Mississippi River at St. Louis, was tapped by over two million people for their drinking water.

"Omaha is the olive in the neck of the bottle," Murray Stein said in 1957. "It is the biggest meat packing center in the world. When we clean up Omaha, the rest of the cities will follow along behind."

The conferences at which Stein presided in the Missouri Valley, that year and the next, defined the issue of water pollution. Does any individual, industry, or local authority have the right to foul our waterways with wastes that "endanger the health or welfare" of others? (Under the Constitution, as we have seen, the federal government may act only in interstate violations, and so must prove that pollution originating in one state affects the people in another; recent federal legislation has modified this requirement in some aspects.) Though the government met antagonism and apathy at these early conferences, there was general agreement that the rivers must be cleaned up. In 1957 city officials along the river pledged their cooperation. Yet in 1965, eight years later, Omaha would still be dumping 300,000 pounds of untreated paunch manure, besides quantities of grease, into the Missouri every day. St. Joseph would be under court order to build treatment facilities. Kansas City would be suddenly pleading poverty, having fallen far behind its construction schedule and having asked permission to delay until 1968 the completion of its treatment plant. Today the Missouri River remains, as the people on its banks say, "Too thick to drink, and too thin to plow."

The Missouri never has been a clear stream. "Ol' Misery," as the early settlers of the West called this shallow yet treacherous river, once flowed northward from its source in the Rocky Mountains. The glaciers that covered much of North America ten thousand years ago turned it aside, and the Missouri cut a new channel along the glaciers' southern edge. Though longer than the Mississippi River and difficult to navigate because of its uncertain currents, the Missouri consists of a relatively light flow of water. It carries with it the soil from a great area of the Northwest, poorly diluted in its flow, so that traditionally the river runs murky. Dams built recently to regulate its flow have reduced the silt but the valley's expanding population began to impose a further burden on the river shortly before World War I. The Missouri's flow no longer could assimilate the valley's wastes. Typhoid broke out on the river in 1912, and again in South Dakota (attributed to the failure of a purifying plant) during the 1930's. To the Missouri's age-old murkiness were added the solids, tastes, smells, and bacteria of a careless civilization.

"This area was settled because the river was there," Murray Stein has said. "The towns that grew up were *river* towns. Then, when the river became polluted, the people had to look someplace else for their livelihood, their recreation and their enjoyment of the country's beauty. They had to turn their backs on the river. Their towns became like any other town that doesn't have a river."

In the 1950's complaints were clearly audible, even in Washington. The Surgeon General of the United States called a series of conferences along the river. The Missouri, flowing through the Dakotas, Nebraska, Iowa, Kansas, and Missouri, obviously carried a heavy burden of pollution from one state to another. It is the aim of a conference of this sort, according to Stein, "to bring together the state water pollution control agencies, the localities and industries concerned, and the Public Health Service to review the existing situation, the progress which has been made, to lay a basis for future action by all parties concerned and to take remedial action which may be indicated under state and local laws."

Under the Federal Water Pollution Control Act, the Public Health Service (through the Secretary of Health, Education and Welfare) may order a hearing if the conference does not prove satisfactory. This is, in effect, an adversary proceeding, heard before a statutory board, with the local authorities and other polluters a party to the action. Witnesses testify under oath, and cross-examination is permitted. If the board's recommendations are not followed by the polluters, the Secretary of HEW may refer the case to the Attorney General, who takes it to court. But this is a step that the government tries to avoid. In more than 35 actions brought against offending cities and areas, the Secretary has sent, as we shall see, only one case to court.

In the summer of 1957 conferences were held in Omaha, St. Joseph, and Kansas City (and a year later in Sioux City, Iowa). The problems in each city were extraordinarily complex. Each dumped into the Missouri, besides its own domestic sewage, the wastes from its enormous packing plants. Here and there a step forward had been taken in the preceding years but the generally obnoxious condition of the river had not changed.

At many places the garbage was placed on dumps near the river and, occasionally, pushed over the banks. J. C. Alexander, a Missouri water engineer, said at the time that "Pollution in the river below St. Joseph has become so serious that the Missouri Division of Resources and

Development is hesitant to suggest the area as a possible industrial site to water-using industries. Pollution is so obvious that one does not need to do more than view the stream to arrive at the correct conclusion that the river is a combination of city dump and open sewer."

Along the populated stretches of the river, chemical analysis revealed high concentrations of coliform bacteria, which come from the intestines of human beings and other warm-blooded animals. Though coliform bacteria do not in themselves cause disease, they are indicators of the presence of gross pollution. A PHS investigator, testifying before the 1957 conference in St. Joseph, said that "The absence of diseases should not create a false sense of safety about the quality of the Missouri River as a source of supply. Dependence must not be placed solely upon water treatment processes, and particularly chlorination, to produce a safe water supply from a highly polluted source. Human errors in operation, mechanical failures, or disaster conditions can result in serious illness by allowing polluted water to break through the barrier of water treatment."

High counts of coliform bacteria were discovered not only below sewer outlets in the river, but also about the drinking-water intakes of cities such as St. Joseph, Omaha, and Kansas City. This discovery proved that part of the pollutional load was reaching river towns from sources many miles upstream. Although bacteria counts were generally lower in the areas of the water intakes, the PHS investigator pointed out that "pollutional damages to uses other than water supply may be considerably greater than can be measured by treatment problems posed at various municipal water plants."

The testimony presented by the federal government at these conferences emphasized the varied and widespread nature of the river's pollution. It showed that even in the early summer of 1957, only a few days before the conference began at St. Joseph, quantities of garbage and paunch manure were being dumped into a manhole on the St. Joseph stockyards sewer. (Paunch manure was mentioned in an earlier chapter as the partially digested hay and corn emptied from an animal's stomach after it has been slaughtered; there are about 65 pounds of paunch manure in the stomach of each beef animal.) The government noted at the conference that the dumping of this material in manholes had been stopped "not for the purpose of eliminating pollution to the Missouri River, but for the purpose of permitting repair to the outfall sewer." After this testimony, the Missouri Division of Health did not permit the practice to be resumed.

Industrial plants, including Armour & Company, Swift & Company, Consumers Co-op, and the Anchor Serum Company, were contributing raw wastes to the Missouri through the St. Joseph municipal sewer system. Standard Brands had been discharging between 6,000 and 10,000 pounds of eggshells a day, and St. Joseph stockyards quantities of manure, through the sewers. The city itself was discharging daily ten million gallons of untreated sewage to the river.

The river vividly reflected this burden. The Public Health Service displayed photographs of animal bladders, lungs, and feet floating down the river. Dwight Metzler of the Kansas Board of Health reported that many cities in his state had requested help in solving their water treatment problems at Missouri River intakes. Citing Atchison as an example, he said that "considerable difficulty has been experienced in the maintenance of adequate chlorine residuals because of fluctuating chlorine demands. Grease and wax have presented problems at the intake and on the filters of the water plants. Eggshells and other materials have complicated operation of the water treatment plant."

T. A. Filipi of the Nebraska Department of Public Health told a similar story. He said the quality of Missouri River water was far below that which health officials desired. "The only reason that it is now used is because there is no other supply available," he told the conference at Omaha. "In the case of Nebraska City another source of water was recently developed in order to get away from drinking the highly polluted river water. When the citizens of Nebraska City learned of the quality of water used as a supply, when they saw the debris on the water plant intake screens, and saw the scum on the settling tanks, prompt action was taken to develop a new water supply."

Fish were so contaminated by oil and tar in the river that an official Missouri report called 20 percent of the fish "not usable;" some commercial fishermen had been driven off the river. Great numbers of Missouri Valley residents, who had once looked to the river for their recreation, now had to find it elsewhere. "It is rather difficult to see how anyone could get much enjoyment from the river when they are among such objectionable refuse from our homes and cities," a Missouri water engineer said.

These early conferences exposed many of the obstacles in the way of successful pollution abatement. On the surface there seemed to be no reason why the individual cities should not move quickly to build effective sewage-treatment plants (some of the smaller cities had already passed the planning stage). At the 1957 Kansas City conference, a city official admitted "objectionable pollution" in the river, which he said was "far in excess of any conceivable limit of tolerance." And he added: "If the conference members desire any further confirmation of that fact, a short observation of the outfalls of the Turkey Creek or Blue River sewer will serve that purpose." The Mayor of Omaha, testifying during the conference in his city, told the conferees (in a statement which might be viewed ironically in the light of later developments), "Several years ago when the federal and state authorities came to the city of Omaha we pledged our assistance and cooperation."

Yet there were innumerable problems just below the surface. Locally, the Public Health Service found a measure of the antagonism which invariably is evoked when the federal government moves into an area long considered to be under the jurisdiction of city and state authorities. On the other hand, Nebraska's T. A. Filipi told the conferees that as far back as 1948 it had been recognized that "the state of Nebraska has no authority to order abatement, and that only when the Congress of the United States so orders will treatment be provided." At the St. Joseph conference a Kansas Health Board official was emphatic in stating the need for sewage-treatment plants.

"If this program is successful," he said, "it needs to be done cooperatively with all the cities moving ahead at the same time getting it done, and this kind of question is five years too late or maybe fifty years too late: do we need to provide sewage treatment at St. Joseph, because the answer is that you do. There is no justification that I can think of for dumping the raw wastes of a community of this size into a stream even the size of the Missouri River."

Essentially, the problem was money, and the plans of the larger cities nearly foundered on the issue of how to finance their treatment plants. The cities' populations had grown, their industries were tremendous, and their sewer systems outdated. Officials in Kansas City, Kansas, for instance, reported that within their city and tributary counties there was a sewered population of 197,230. Yet this area, combining its domestic and industrial wastes, dumped into the Missouri River sewage the strength of which was calculated to equal that of a population of 780,000. Many experts testified that individual industries should be responsible for removing "their own peculiar wastes not compatible with city treatment." A Kansas City, Missouri, official said that, "Industries discharging wastes into the Blue River are aware of the condition of the river and of the need for corrective measures. However, in general, they have adopted an attitude of watchful waiting; and insofar as is known, none plan any immediate anti-pollution steps of major significance."

Industry's attitude of "watchful waiting" was disastrously paralleled by the general public's reluctance to do anything it might have to pay for. To build treatment plants, and lay the interceptor sewers which would bring sewage to the plants from the collecting sewers before it emptied into the river, is enormously expensive. The money obviously could not come from a city's normal budget. It had to be borrowed, and the way to borrow the money was to sell bonds to investors, the city to pay the interest on the bonds it issued. Only the public, through its votes, could approve the creation of such bonds and fix their size. No one was eager to authorize a bond issue, on which the money to pay interest would be raised through taxes, unless he was convinced that the city was getting something in return for its investment. A sewage-treatment plant generally benefits only the towns downstream. Local people had to be convinced that only by all of the towns moving ahead with construction, those upstream as well as down, could their river be effectively cleaned up. Apparently, they had not been convinced. St. Joseph, for instance, had voted down such a bond issue in November, 1953, and other towns had done the same.

The problem in St. Joseph was complicated by the fact that many of the polluting industries lay outside the city limits. The people, in effect, were being asked to build a treatment plant into which industries not subject to city taxes might pour their wastes. This, of course, would require a larger plant. Though city officials suggested that the industries first treat their wastes to make them easier to handle at the plant and then pay part of the plant's cost, the people of St. Joseph viewed the whole affair with suspicion.

"It is my opinion," a local businessman told the St. Joseph conference, "that so long as the packing industries, that is the 17 industries, are outside of our city limits, that any bond issue for the construction of a sewage disposal plant in November hasn't got any more chance than a snowball in hell."

A vicious circle took shape. The people refused to vote for a bond issue unless they had been convinced of its need, yet in many cases the local politicians were unwilling to help convince them: to do so would be to ally themselves with an unpopular cause. According to

Dwight Metzler of the Kansas Board of Health, "Out of 200 bond elections that have been passed in Kansas in the last nine years for sewage treatment we had not seen a single one fail where the city governing body was essentially behind the proposal."

Typical of a city's problems in trying to build sewage-treatment plants were those of Kansas City, Missouri. Mayor Roe Bartle, a bear of a man weighing over 300 pounds, is remembered by Murray Stein as one of the most engaging and candid local officials to appear at any of the Public Health Service conferences. Taking his place at the table, he told the conference, "I just work here. I occupy a large space on the 29th floor."

Mayor Bartle had played a prominent role in two rather searing incidents in the history of Kansas City—the transfer there from Philadelphia of a very bad baseball team called the Athletics, and the early negotiations for municipal sewage treatment. For his pains in the first instance he received his own box seat, or rather a pair of box seats, at the ball park. Charles O. Finley, the Athletics' owner, ordered the arm rest between two citrus yellow seats removed to accommodate the mayor's great bulk. For his pains in the second instance, the mayor suffered the further tortures peculiar to a politician who must go to the public for money. When asked by the conferees if a public vote on the bond issue could be held shortly before the terms of the present city council members expired (so that, if a new council were elected, the issue would not have to be pushed by those unfamiliar with its details), Bartle replied:

"I just can't imagine anybody going to run for office and then on the eve of their running for office ask the city to vote a huge bond issue. It would be the best way in the world to defeat those that want to stand for re-election. Because again I must point out that America today is allergic to taxes. Primarily because of the heavy federal taxes which we are required to pay it makes it very difficult to get local taxes to take care of fire and police and health on a local basis. I checked the figures the other day and discovered that back in 1940 local government was getting 51 cents out of every tax dollar and now they are getting 13 cents out of every tax dollar, and the federal government is mounting, mounting, mounting!"

A program to instruct the people in the benefits of proper sewage treatment, Bartle said, must be undertaken by the state and federal governments. "I for one labor under the theory," he said, "that if the city council would ask the municipality to vote *x*-millions of dollars for sewage disposal it would be overwhelmingly defeated. I think it has to be a program which does not stem from the city hall but stems from every nook and corner of the country on the part of citizens who do recognize the problem and realize that something must be done about it."

Another obstacle that federal and state authorities constantly encountered was the long delay between the time that engineering reports were submitted to city officials and their final clearance. Mayor Bartle offered his explanation for this condition, too. "I will remind you, sir," he told Chairman Murray Stein, "that this city council is composed of nine men, six of whom are lawyers, and when these engineering reports come to those of us who are members of the bar it takes a long time to understand what they are talking about.

"I should explain to you, sir," he went on, poking at his

dentures, "that many years ago in the days of my youth I tried to play football and God gave me two very fine sets of teeth and the second set of teeth were destroyed by a group of thugs and yeggs and boilermakers and blacksmiths and men that were on the Georgia chain gang who were playing for Georgia Tech and as a result I have been paying annually considerable to have some store-made teeth and last night they went haywire on me and I am having difficulty enunciating. I would like to charge that also to engineers from Georgia Tech."

Amid laughter, Stein said, "I might say that I am a lawyer working with engineers all the time and would hate to admit that we lawyers will need as much time to make up our minds on the report as the engineers have to take to digest the report."

"It doesn't take a lawyer any time to make up his mind," the mayor said, "but sometimes these engineers confuse me a little with all their verbiage. I unfortunately don't understand the King's English or Queen's English, as it is now, as well as some of these engineers. When I get through I wonder what they have told me. And if you have to work with engineers all the time I will say to you that I will put you on my prayer list as an elder in the church. I think you are entitled to it."

"Thank you," Stein said.

"We do have to have engineers and I wouldn't belittle engineers at all," the mayor went on, "and when I look at all the money this city appropriates to engineers with great regularity may I say to you, sir, that it is the lawyers that are starving, not the engineers today, let me assure you."

"No one realizes that more acutely than I do, sir," Stein told him.

"Well, I am happy that at least I have found a companion."

Although somewhat dazed by the mayor's eloquence, the conferees pressed him to help to bring Kansas City's construction schedule into line with those of neighboring communities. Bartle agreed that "we are all in the same pot," and hoped for the best. Having exhausted the supply of questions (and perhaps the questioners) he lifted himself from his chair and excused himself from the conference on the grounds of prior commitments.

"I shall be like General MacArthur, I shall return, but I am committed to go," the mayor announced.

"I would like to say we would like to have you come here if your schedule permits any time during the day and sit in and see how we are progressing," Stein said.

"Thank you, sir," Mayor Bartle nodded before departing. "And I appreciate it immensely. And when I am gone my own fifth columnists are here."

II

After Mayor Bartle had retired from office, "to play with my grandchildren," the fun went out of the Missouri River project for Murray Stein and his colleagues. A few of the messier sites were tidied up, it is true. But chiefly the conferences produced promises and statements, most of them not nearly as entertaining as those of Mayor Bartle. Among the larger towns, only Sioux City proceeded to set its house in order and even there the project nearly foundered. Stein and HEW forced Sioux City to a hearing, then threatened court action. When events there took a favorable turn, the government was suddenly embarrassed by the revelation that one of the region's most prominent polluters, discharging untreated sewage to the river, was a United States Air Force base. An efficient municipal government, however, steered Sioux City through its besetting problems and in 1962 it received the All-America City Award, partly on the basis of its new waste-treatment facilities.

"Right after they got the award," Stein recalls, "we received a letter from the city manager, thanking us for our help."

It was not until 1960 that Kansas City got around to scheduling a vote on its bond issue. Even then, when the city had continued to pollute the river for three years after Mayor Bartle's appearance at the PHS conference, and was subjected to the adversary proceedings of a formal hearing, a great deal of pressure had to be applied to citizens and administration alike. Finally, in that year, the citizens of Kansas City voted $75 million in sewer and pollution-control bonds, thereby increasing their water bills by 48 percent. The city felt quite proud of itself. It reserved the right to determine what material might be poured into sewers, and decided to levy a surcharge on heavily polluted wastes. The people looked forward to the completion of their sewage-disposal plants by the end of 1966.

In 1965 the people of Kansas City became aware that something had gone wrong. There had been a miscalculation in the cost of the treatment plants. In an effort to soothe the voters several years earlier, the city had appended a nominal service charge to the customary water bills, hoping to finance its bond issue. The service charge, it turned out, was far too low. "The rate was based not on profit but on politics," Stein said recently.

Kansas City Mayor Ilus Davis, the city manager, and the city director of pollution control suggested an increase in the sewage service charges. The city council objected, one of its members claiming that the burden of sewage taxes fell on homeowners, who also pay large water bills. The city council asked instead for a delay in completing its sewage plant construction. It asked the federal government to allow the city at least until May, 1968, to begin treatment.

Stein flew to Kansas City and confronted members of the city council. After hearing their story, he insisted that Kansas City follow its mayor and not its city council. He ordered the city to complete its sewage plant construction by January 1, 1967. Otherwise, he said, he would recommend that the Federal Housing Administration terminate its loans to the city. "In the event that progress is not made," Stein said, "the states will join with us in asking the Attorney General for court action."

"This is one of the worst examples of federal dictatorship I have ever seen," a lady member of the council told the press. Kansas City is still at war with itself.

If Kansas City meets its construction deadline, the memory of St. Joseph will have played a considerable part in its accomplishment. It was at St. Joseph that Stein, acting for the federal government, pressed his case to the ultimate level against unregenerate polluters. The city of St. Joseph, after the PHS conference there, scheduled a vote on its bond issue for March 4, 1958. The issue was to total $9,150,000. Of this amount, about $6 million was to provide the construction of interceptor sewers, pumping stations, and a sewage-treatment plant. The remainder (and the issue's chief liability) was to provide sewers for outlying areas then without any municipal facilities and for others which the city planned to annex in the near future. St. Joseph's industries were to reimburse the city for $1 million in order to have their wastes pumped to the treatment plant.

A citizens' committee was appointed to educate the voters on the advantages of proper sewage disposal. The committee waged, according to one observer, "a reasonably good campaign." As for the press, he said that "it became increasingly favorable to the bond issue as the head of steam of the publicity program was generated and I think that if it had lasted another week it might have been enthusiastic." At the same time there was some vigorous opposition to the proposal. Aside from the usual reluctance of people to tax themselves for such relatively invisible property as sewage-disposal units ("There is no sales appeal in sewers," *Fortune* Magazine has said), there was the issue of the outlying areas. It was not yet certain that these areas would be annexed by the city. A mysterious "yellow sheet" appeared a few days before the election, attacking the bond issue. Many people considered the issue too large a burden for a city of 80,000 (although Missouri cities of smaller population and assessed property valuation had voted proportionately larger bond issues for sewage treatment).

On election day about half of St. Joseph's 30,000 registered voters turned out to cast their ballots. A four-sevenths majority was needed to carry the issue. The final count was 7,826 voting "yes," and 7,218 voting "no." Falling 385 votes short of the needed majority, the bond issue was defeated.

And with its defeat the city's will to struggle wilted.

City officials and industrial leaders drifted apart on plans to construct a common sewage-treatment plant, and industry decided to go ahead on its own (but not very rapidly). The Missouri Water Pollution Board ordered the city to schedule a new election before May 31, 1959. There was no response to its order. In March the State Board finally threw up its hands in despair and asked Washington to intervene. In its letter to the Public Health Service, the state noted that, "Since it is evident that the City of St. Joseph does not plan to hold a bond election prior to May 31, it is respectfully requested that a hearing in accordance with Public Law 660 [the Federal Water Pollution Control Act of 1956] be held relative to the pollution contributed by the City of St. Joseph and the stockyard industries at the earliest possible convenient date."

The hearing was held at St. Joseph on July 27-30, 1959. The government's case was heard by a board consisting of five members, four of them representing the water pollution control boards of Missouri, Kansas, Indiana, and Nebraska; the fifth represented the United States Department of Commerce. All were appointed by the Secretary of Health, Education and Welfare, and were asked to come up with a finding of whether the defendants were causing pollution of an interstate nature and, if so, what steps were recommended to abate it.

The government's case, presented by Murray Stein, was impressive. Federal investigators testified that the wastes from this city of almost 80,000 people, including those from "toilets, bathrooms, garages, street washings, and other commercial establishments" were being dumped untreated into the Missouri River, to mingle there with the untreated wastes of industries lying on the city's outskirts.

They estimated the volume of sewage to be ten million gallons a day. The investigators and scientists pointed out that only 24 miles below St. Joseph was Atchison, which took its drinking water from the river, while beyond lay Leavenworth and Kansas City.

The condition of the river, as described by government witnesses, was frightening. One witness saw "Considerable floating grease and scum, pieces of animal intestines, lungs, gas bubbles from the bottom of the channel would occasionally rise and lift septic sludge, paunch manure, and so forth." A channel inspector employed by the United States Corps of Engineers testified that he and his colleagues, being in frequent contact with river water, were innoculated by the government against typhoid. There was testimony from others of excessive grease and scum collecting on the hulls of boats and of slime and feces collecting on sandbars in the middle of the river. Duck hunters felt themselves endangered by the obnoxious material they had to clean from their decoys. Asked to describe the wastes collecting at the Atchison filter plant, its operator replied, "Well, the presence of ladies precludes mention of some of the things I have seen. However, I will leave it to your imagination. They were floating substances."

Against this formidable government case the city and industry attorneys threw up the kind of smokescreen which has contributed immeasurably to the disgraceful condition of American rivers. In 1958 there had been considerable opposition to the bond issue on the grounds that part of the money was to provide sewers for outlying areas which might not even be annexed by St. Joseph. Now, in 1959, opposition was based on the fact that those areas, including 10,000 people, had just been annexed, and the new citizens feared higher taxes. One might reasonably have called this a "captive population," for these 10,000 people so detested the idea of becoming citizens of St. Joseph that they had fought the annexation all the way to the state supreme court. The federal government had asked St. Joseph to set up a schedule for planning a sewage-treatment plant. St. Joseph and its industries were being asked to complete their plans by September 1, 1959, and hold a new bond election before November 15. Those opposed pleaded that there was not time to educate the electorate, and especially those 10,000 already-angry new citizens. Besides, the city as a whole was embittered because St. Joseph had been ordered to provide treatment before many of the other cities along the Missouri. An attorney representing St. Joseph's industries pleaded for an extension of time on the grounds that people had to be told "why we must go to all these additional costs for four or five years before those downriver cities do. We can't go to industry very well and say, 'Look, we have got all these additional costs. You go to Kansas City or St. Louis and escape for five years, maybe ten years.' "

"I thought that—" Glen Hopkins, a Public Health Service official, broke in.

"Further," the industry attorney continued, "I don't think it is reasonable when you have not completed the arrangements at Omaha and you are having trouble at Sioux City."

"I am surprised at this problem of selling industry on this matter," Hopkins said. "It has been my understanding that industry was rather progressive and had already done much of this."

"Industry has, certain types of industry, there is no question about it," the attorney said. "On the other hand, there is a lot of industry that looks at their costs in coming into a city, as you well realize."

The industry attorney went on to plead for extra time, saying that the PHS schedule was too tight, and asking Hopkins if he didn't think that it put industry "in a rather awkward situation and an almost *impossible* situation."

"I don't believe so," Hopkins said. "I would like to give you reasons why. I believe that industry has been cognizant of this problem for several years, has been studying it, they have information from other plants in the packing house industry as to what the logical approaches to reducing these wastes are, and what the results of those can be. I do not believe that at St. Joseph this constitutes an unreasonable burden on the industries."

"You would agree, would you not, that 45 days is a rather short time for large industries to make plans for substantial changes of this character?"

"It is my opinion," Hopkins said, "that basically this was determined before a cost allocation between the city and the industry was agreed upon prior to the last bond election. I don't see how the costs could have been allocated without that information being at hand because that proposal also required the reduction of industrial wastes before discharge to the city system."

The industry counsel did not pursue the question. He went on to other matters. "You see, Mr. Hopkins, you are dealing with Missourians, your 'Show Me's, and some people say mules, and they want to know the facts. Now, you have suddenly produced on your side of the case a certain amount of evidence, which is quite substantial. I would be the last man in the world to deny it. Do you think that the people of St. Joseph assimilate this evidence and understand this when they voted it down a short time ago, that they can be re-oriented and put on a new hat and get all this done in that time—you have got to take 30 days out before you can even get the ordinance passed."

"I think the—well, the education campaign that you mentioned need not await the actual passage of the ordinance," Hopkins said. "I think the people of St. Joe would be much more capable of making a concerted assimilation digestion of the facts of this case in six weeks than if they scattered it out as a piecemeal job over one or two years."

"You don't think you can catch more flies with honey than you can with vinegar?"

"I think," Hopkins replied, "the supply of honey has probably been exhausted in this situation."

In summing up its defense, industry resorted chiefly to deprecating the effects of its pollution on the river, and threatening the Public Health Service with the loss of its power. In the first instance, industry counsel turned to the chairman of the hearing board and said, "Now you come from this part of the country and you are pretty familiar with the history of the Missouri River. It has always been known as the Big Muddy and mud denotes silt and silt denotes contamination. This was a great buffalo country. I think when Joliet and Marquette passed the mouth of the river the journal shows that there was a large river coming in from the west filled with mud and logs and floated buffaloes . . . that all denotes contamination and that contamination existed long before we were here. It exists at the present time. Instead of buffalo droppings and fecal matter it comes from hogs, cattle, livestock of various kinds."

Having registered the unfortunate buffalo as co-defendant, industry counsel took a harder line. "Now, bear in mind, gentlemen, this Water Pollution Control Act was passed by the people of this country because they believed in clean streams and clean water and if you are going to try and sell it to them by force you are liable to find the people are going to raise up and say, well, we can't achieve what we thought we could, the cost is too great, and you might have no water pollution control law."

The federal government's summary was more positive. City and industry counsels had discounted the dangers of polluted water on the grounds that disease was not evident along the Missouri River. The government had already mentioned the many diseases present in fecal pollution, including such organisms as salmonella (which cause typhoid), shigella, and brucella. "Maybe we have short memories," Murray Stein said at the hearing's close, "I don't know, but I seem to have heard the Atchison plant operator say he was operating at top capacity and there was a breakthrough in his plant. To get a reportable disease, such as typhoid or something of that sort, is a catastrophe I don't think we have to wait for. We all know the enteric diseases and diarrhea are nonreportable diseases and are water-borne. The evidence has indicated that very clearly."

The verdict of the hearing board was that St. Joseph and its industries were indeed polluting the Missouri River and endangering the health and welfare of persons in neighboring states. When the city continued to drag its feet, the Secretary of Health, Education and Welfare turned the case over to the Attorney General. It was the first and only time that the United States Government had gone all the way to court to force polluters to clean up their mess. The case was heard in United States District Court by Judge R. M. Duncan. At a pre-trial hearing St. Joseph officials presented their case.

"What are you going to do—put the city council in jail?" one of them asked.

"No," the judge replied. "But I can dip into your till."

The city capitulated. In planning its sewage-treatment facilities, St. Joseph and its industries agreed to disagree. Asking for a whole loaf, the city got none. Its terms to industry for a cooperative venture proved too severe, and industry closed ranks to build its own plant, which went into operation late in 1963. Having its own treatment plant, its own fire and police departments and a lower tax schedule, the outlying industrial complex now sees no reason to have itself annexed by St. Joseph. The city has blundered on without this rich source of taxes, and remains under court orders to complete its municipal plant in 1966.

After this series of intramural struggles, the result has not been satisfactory. According to Mayor Arthur J. Meers, the building of separate treatment plants was a mistake: by pooling the municipal and industry funds with a grant from the federal government, both construction and maintenance costs would have been less for all parties. "Actually," Meers says, "it is an economic loss to those industries and it is an economic loss to the area."

A recent visitor to St. Joseph adds a further note. "The city," he says, "smells bad."

III

Despite the squabbles elsewhere, and despite its escape from either a formal hearing or a court case, Omaha remains "the olive in the neck of the bottle." Technically, it is cooperating with state and federal agencies. It has gone ahead to plan, finance, and build a fine new sewage-treatment plant. Yet each day the city's packing houses continue to pour 300 tons of paunch manure and 100 tons of grease into the Missouri. Despite the millions of dollars it has spent on sewage treatment the quantities of untreated wastes discharged to the river remain today approximately the same as they were in 1957.

What had happened in the intervening years? The federal government, in an effort to find out, called another session of the conference at Omaha during the summer of 1964. There had, it developed, been an unexpected change in the city's plans. When the bright new Missouri River Sewage Treatment Plant had been designed, the city had understood that the packing industry would pretreat its wastes in the packing house before discharging them into the city sewers. This was not done. Though the packers removed certain amounts of blood and grease in their plants, they continued to dump the paunch manure, as they had always done, into the sewers. The city, unable to handle this volume of solids, simply closed down one-half of its expensive new treatment plant and allowed this enormous amount of sewage to pass untreated into the river.

"We did get a small amount of paunch manure from the South Omaha sewer in the early days of testing this plant," a city engineer explained, "and it was a tremendous problem in trying to get it out of the lines after it got in, and I would not like to take any more of the paunch manure."

There were outraged cries downstream. St. Joseph, set on regeneration, protested Omaha's flagrant pollution of the river. In a letter to the Missouri State Water Pollution Board, the manager of the St. Joseph Water Company complained of packing plant tallow entering its facilities during most of 1963 and 1964. "It collected against baffles on our settling basins making it necessary to resort to skimming at times. The material leaves a greasy film on the walls of our basins and filters . . . The particles of tallow floating on the basins vary in sizes from the size of a small hen's egg to tiny pieces like grains of sand. The small particles are, of course, the most numerous and cause the greatest problems. Animal hair is present in the larger pieces."

After a detailed investigation, the Missouri Water Pollution Board concluded that the grease and tallow were coming from outside the state and pointed a tentative finger at Omaha. Kansas joined the attack on Omaha, reporting high densities of coliform bacteria at the water intakes of many of its cities. A Kansas official testified that at Atchison the sedimentation basins had to shut down while the walls were cleaned of grease. Criticism of Omaha came from within the state of Nebraska too. A man from the state Department of Health expressed the department's "disappointment" when it learned that Omaha had changed its plans and would not be able to stop polluting the Missouri according to the original schedule.

A PHS spokesman summed up the problem at the conference. "The city of Omaha, Nebraska," he said, "has made substantial progress in constructing pollution abatement facilities and the necessary appurtenances. However, the construction of inplant waste production practices and/or facilities by the packing industry has not kept pace with the Omaha Municipal Construction Program."

As the conference proceeded, the reason for the collapse of Omaha's plans became clear. Omaha is the country's largest meat-packing center. Its markets receive livestock from 26 states, and from there the animals are sometimes sent alive to packers in 130 cities in 30 other states. "It is as important to the livestock industry, the farmers and the feeders and other central markets like it," an Omaha man says, "as Wall Street is to the stock and bond industry. You have to have a place to base your price, and large volume and heavy demand does that."

It is small wonder then that one's civic pride sometimes leads one to make extraordinary boasts. One of the problems in slaughtering a large number of cattle is that a city is left with a large volume of paunch manure on its hands. At the PHS conference, the president of Omaha's city council rose to speak of the problem. "Now, with reference to the tonnage of paunch manure," he said, "I would like to call your attention to the fact, if you don't already know it, that Omaha is blessed with the greatest packing industry in the world—right here in Omaha—and when we talk about paunch manure we are talking about paunch manure from this great, great industry." He spoke in the accents that a civic booster in another town might slip into while boasting of the Golden Gate Bridge or Grant's Tomb.

The packers of Omaha, after first agreeing that they

would remove the paunch manure at their own plants (selling it as fertilizer or for some other use), finally ruled against doing this on the grounds that it would be too expensive. The city, like any other which is dependent on a single large industry, was powerless to hold the packers to their word. There were two alternatives. One was to truck the paunch manure from the packing plants and burn or bury it on the outskirts of the city. Omaha officials refused to do this, claiming that it would be expensive and "not aesthetic" to truck the paunch manure through the streets. "Certainly we wouldn't want to carry it in open containers because of the odor problem particularly," an engineer employed by the city said, "and carrying it in closed containers we have the opportunity of bursting a container with quite a nuisance resulting from that."

"I don't know that a tank would burst," Murray Stein said, "but it would seem to me, wouldn't it, that the same kind of material dumped untreated into the Missouri River might create a pollution problem?"

"No question about that, sir, that this—"

"And this is what we are proposing to do," Stein said, "at least until 1966."

The other alternative, and the one finally decided upon by the city, was to allow the packers to dump the paunch manure in the city sewers, from where it would be carried along to the sewage-treatment plant, removed from the sewage there by sedimentation, dried, and burned. To accomplish this, the city was building a modern incinerator, at a cost of one and a half million dollars. The 19 packing companies in Omaha agreed to assume the cost of this operation for 20 years. The incinerator, however, was not to be completed until 1967.

"The point is, who will it save money for?" Stein asked,

referring to the incinerator. "Will it save the taxpayers any money by going to this incinerator operation? In other words, you are going to give the people of Omaha less of a bill?"

"I don't know whether that question can be answered categorically, Mr. Stein," the Omaha engineer replied.

"What?"

"Certainly, all costs are eventually borne by the public," the engineer went on, "whether they be directly assessed by taxation or whether they be carried through increased sale costs of the products which are produced."

"I could agree with that, sir," Stein said.

"And therefore the use of the higher cost method of disposal becomes an economic loss to the area eventually, and—"

"Let's see if I understand you on the economics," Stein said. "I am fascinated by this. If this is going to cost one and a half million dollars more, cost to the city of Omaha, and you say eventually all costs must be borne by the public, this clearly will be borne by the people of the city of Omaha. If this, however, is put on a product like a meat product which is sold throughout the country, this one and a half million dollar cost will be dispersed throughout the country and borne by the country as a whole. Now, maybe the people of Omaha want to assume this, but if you say part of the reasons are additional costs, I think the next question comes, additional costs to whom?"

"I would like to stay out of this area of financing, Mr. Stein," another engineer broke in, "but it is up to you, because, as you know, we can continue it."

"You gave this as one of the reasons," Stein reminded him.

"Let's take the other side of it," the second engineer said. "We don't want to lose an industry either. There are those economics which are to be considered."

While referring to Omaha's new plan as "this noble experiment," Stein and other PHS officials expressed some doubt whether the process would work satisfactorily. The process seemed to them to include an unnecessary step. Rather than remove the paunch manure at the packing plant, where it is in a better condition to be dried and burned, the packers were putting it into the sewers where it would be soaked in water, then taken out again and dried thoroughly before it was burned.

"You can burn anything if you want to pay enough money for it," Stein pointed out. "All you have got to do is keep squeezing enough water out and applying enough heat, and you can burn it. As a matter of fact, one of the methods of purifying water is distilling it. It is a question of cost."

Those interested in cleaning up the Missouri were disturbed by the long delay at Omaha while the fine new treatment plant ran at only half its capacity; further, there was some doubt that this novel method of removing paunch manure would solve the city's problem. Stein also pointed out that the entire program was uneconomical; having already borrowed to finance much of the $20 million paid for treatment facilities and interceptor sewers, the city was not getting full value for its money. As one of the conferees said, "There is interest of approximately three percent being paid out on a $20 million investment which has been expended over a period of years, since 1958, which is not yet in operation." Three percent of $20 million is $600,000 a year.

And so, because the removal of the paunch manure at

the packing plants had proved to be what one conferee called "an indigestible problem" to the industry, the people of Omaha continue to pay for an unused facility, and the people downstream continue to pick grease and animal hair out of their water-supply filters. The packers shrugged it off. "We have lived with it for 80 years or more in this industry," one of them said at the conference, "and I hope that you will go along with us another year or 18 months, which won't make any difference, and don't put the additional burden on industry."

This was in response to a suggestion that the packers might temporarily remove the paunch manure at the source, at least until the incinerator was in operation. To the charge that industry was polluting water which other people drank and used for recreation, the same packer replied, "Certainly they do not want to pollute waters for drinking or for boating and fishing, but I could say, and I will not be facetious when I say it, that in this particular area, if we don't have this industry, very few people will have enough money to go fishing . . .

"The packing industry is here, gentlemen," this spokesman for industry went on, "for two or three reasons. One, of course, is the broad supply, but another is the cost of operations, and if you load onto industry an additional burden, they could leave here as fast as they left Chicago. They could move to the hinterlands."

"We carry out the law the way Congress has asked us to carry out the law," Murray Stein told him. "I don't know how many of the state people are entranced by having a federal agency in this picture, but one of the big motivations, as I can see it, for having the federal agency in the picture is the constant argument that if we do this, industry will go out. The Congress wants to be sure that people like myself will be waiting for industry wherever they move."

As the conference drew to a close one fact became obvious: though Omaha was slowly moving toward compliance with earlier state and federal recommendations, its treatment plant, even working at full capacity, might not be able to cope with the sewage directed to it in times of heavy storm runoff, or under the pressure of a growing population. Stein recalled that when the program to clean up the Missouri began, there had been a clamor from many people to require secondary as well as primary treatment plants in every city (the methods used in secondary treatment remove many of the dissolved pollutants which remain in water after primary treatment).

"I think we tried to hit a reasonable compromise," Stein said, "and go for primary treatment and save the people in the valley millions and millions of dollars. We expected though that when you went with primary treatment, we would operate in a reasonable way and not push this to the limits of endurance . . . If we are going to push the pendulum the other way and try to stretch primary treatment to the biggest load we can put in the river, I don't know how much of a service you are doing to yourselves or this whole river valley."

Stein told the conferees that plans were first made for Omaha's sewage-disposal plant in 1957. Ten years will have passed before the plant is in complete operation. By that time the local population and industry will have grown so that there is the possibility the treatment plant will not be able to cope with the added burden. "By the time we get through with the growth we have and the primary treatment and what you are putting in," Stein said, "we are going to end up with the same load in the river as we were ten years ago when we got started. With all the 20-odd million dollars we have spent, we might be 20 million dollars poorer, but, like Alice in Wonderland, we will have been running awfully hard to stay in the same place."

Four: "Bacteria Beach"

"The number of these hepatitis cases having a history of eating raw clams is too high to be ignored," Dr. Roscoe P. Kandle, New Jersey's Health Commissioner told the press. "It could not be mere chance. I have no alternative except to close the indicated areas to the taking of shellfish until further notice."

It was April 30, 1961. Dr. Kandle's announcement brought an extraordinary epidemic of infectious hepatitis to public notice, cleared up a mystery which had puzzled doctors in several states, and applied the crushing blow to an enterprise which in the past had been one of the most profitable in the New York metropolitan area. Once again the arrogant assumption by certain industries and municipalities that all the land, air, and water around them is simply a God-given receptacle for their filth had led to public disaster. Hundreds of people were seriously ill, yet even then the polluters had not been jolted from their indifference. Despite the publicity, investigations, cajoling, and threats which were directed at them in the intervening years, the New Jersey Health Department said at the beginning of 1965 that there was "no substantial improvement" since it had issued orders to clean up the blighted area.

The area to which Dr. Kandle alluded when he closed its shellfish beds is Raritan Bay. It is a triangular body of tidal water, about 12 miles square, merging at its eastern end into New York's Lower Bay. To the north it is bounded by Staten Island (which is one of New York City's five boroughs) and to the west and south by New Jersey. It was in this area that fortunes were made in shellfish (mostly oysters) during the 19th century. The shellfish, plump and highly prized, were sold both here and in England, and the Staten Islanders who were their chief harvesters, built stately mansions and lived in luxury.

But if you "are what you eat," so are oysters. Raritan Bay and its shellfish began to change at the turn of the century. Industries, which go where there is water, congregated on the shores of Raritan Bay and its tributaries, and people, who go where there are industries, congregated too. Nearby oil refineries imparted to the shellfish a distinct taste of kerosene; human wastes imparted a suspicious plumpness ("They were as fat as butter," one man said). The shellfish, its natural food destroyed by pollution, adapted by feeding on the pollution itself.

According to Dr. Harold H. Haskin, professor of biology at Rutgers, an adult oyster "will pump an average of 20 quarts an hour through its gills and will remove quantitatively practically all microscopic materials. In so doing it will concentrate bacterial contaminants and many dissolved chemicals."

Because both shellfish larvae and sewage tend to mass in areas where the currents eddy rather than flow toward the sea, oysters and clams often grow in polluted waters. "By virtue of their power to concentrate many materials suspended and dissolved in the water," Dr. Haskin says, "the oyster, clam, and other filter feeders become valuable early indicators of pollution—in some cases, I think, a little more effective than some of our chemists."

The oyster business around Raritan Bay collapsed in the summer of 1916. An outbreak of typhoid fever among New Yorkers was conclusively traced to the oysters they had eaten—oysters over whose beds flowed the outpouring of a New Jersey trunk sewer. The taking of oysters from Raritan Bay and Lower Bay was prohibited. The clams, growing in more remote beds near the New Jersey shore, were still considered edible. Clammers from Staten Island and New Jersey went out in small boats at dawn to harvest the shellfish with long-handled rakes. They did not grow wealthy, like the oystermen of another era, but they made a comfortable living. That part of Raritan Bay off Staten Island was the only area in New York City from which shellfish were harvested. In 1950 the Raritan Bay clam industry earned $300,000 in the New York market. By 1960 that figure had declined to $174,000, and the following year, with Dr. Kandle's announcement, the clammers were wiped out.

Infectious hepatitis is a serious disease. It is an inflammation of the liver caused by a virus, and jaundice is among its symptoms. While it can be contracted in a number of ways, it often attacks people who have taken contaminated food or drink, and children are particularly susceptible. But in the epidemic that struck New Jersey early in 1961 the patients were predominantly adult. There were 1,082 cases in the first four months of that year, more than twice as many as had been reported the year before, and 80 percent of them were adults. Launching an investigation into its causes, the New Jersey Health Department went into a neighborhood in which there were 370 cases. Most of the victims were men in above-average income levels (which, the department noted, is also a description of those who buy and consume the great majority of raw shellfish). The department's investigators selected an equal number of people in that environment who had not contracted hepatitis, and found that only ten percent of them had eaten raw clams in recent months. Of the 370 hepatitis cases, 210 had eaten clams. Another investigator reported that 186 hepatitis cases had eaten raw clams at two New Jersey restaurants, both of which bought almost all their clams from Raritan Bay dealers. It was at this point that Dr. Kandle closed the New Jersey portions of Raritan Bay. Later that day, a similar announcement was made by health officials in New York State.

This, to date, has been the familiar official reaction to gross pollution. The primary step is not to root out pollution, but to declare the polluted area a public sewer and forget about it. This is the approach which Maine's Senator Edmund Muskie has attacked in his home state, where the paper companies' "right" to turn rivers into sewers has been given priority over the clammers' right to harvest shellfish, or the children's right to swim in the rivers. Stewart Udall, the Secretary of the Interior, has put it another way: "This is the destruction of one resource usually in order to improvidently harvest another resource or carry on some industrial process that is harmful to other resources. To achieve the full potential of the natural resources of our country, it seems to me we have to seek ways and means of developing and exploiting a resource without harming other resources."

It is likely that, having solved the Raritan Bay problem by obliterating the clammers, state officials in New York and New Jersey would have let it fade from public notice had not the hepatitis epidemic there coincided with similar outbreaks in other parts of the country. National reports indicated that there were twice as many cases in 1961 as there had been the year before. The United States Public Health Service, investigating an outbreak in Mississippi and Alabama earlier in 1961, traced it to oysters harvested by a single worker on Mississippi's Pascagoula River. The oysterman had been taking his haul from beds located only a mile and a half from an outlet for raw sewage near the city of Pascagoula. But, to the Public Health Service, the most critical area was Raritan Bay, washing the shores of both the country's largest city (New York) and its most densely populated state (New Jersey). Although reports of hepatitis had come from all over the country, the majority of cases seemed to be in those states bordering or close to Raritan Bay. The Department of Health, Education and Welfare, through the Public Health Service, called a conference of the affected states.

The Public Health Service, in making its investigation, took in portions of Sandy Hook Bay and New York's Lower Bay, as well as tributaries of Raritan Bay such as the Raritan River and Arthur Kill. These waters are about evenly divided between New Jersey and New York. Public Health Service officials did not receive a hearty welcome. State officials, as well as their representatives on the Interstate Sanitation Commission, a state-sanctioned agency which has struggled for a number of years without notable success to abate pollution in the waters of New York, New Jersey, and Connecticut, were outspokenly unhappy at what they felt was the meddling of the federal government.

"There's usually a conflict," one PHS investigator says. "State officials will tell you there's no problem, and our job is to go in and find out what the problem *is*."

Even if the states were willing to attack the problem vigorously, their appropriate agencies do not have the staff, the equipment, or the funds. New Jersey, for instance, has a staff of 16 men covering various aspects of water pollution in the state, and working on a budget of about $350,000 a year. According to PHS estimates, a state with its size and problems should have a minimum of 82 trained workers (128 would be a more desirable figure) and a budget at least triple its present amount. Moreover, the New Jersey Health Department, even if properly staffed, has no power to levy fines. Though it can take offenders to court, it has not done so in 20 years. In 1959 the state told industries along the Arthur Kill that it must improve the treatment of their wastes, but did not issue "orders" to the offenders until four years later. Yet state officials, both in New Jersey and New York, presumed to grumble at federal intervention.

There was no doubt that New York was contributing heavily to the pollution in Raritan Bay. New York City itself discharges one-half billion gallons of raw sewage a day into the bays and rivers that surround it; nearly all of the sewage from about 70th Street downtown to the Battery, the sewage from the Red Hook section of Brooklyn, and a considerable quantity from Staten Island reaches the public waters insufficiently treated. Much of this, flowing through the Narrows, penetrates Raritan Bay or the other areas studied by the Public Health Service. Effluent (Julian Huxley has called this "The Effluent Society") from the sewers of factories and towns along the Raritan River was somewhat cleaned up in the 1950's after a former Surgeon General called its waters "among the most polluted in the nation," but it still posed many problems.

If any body of water in the country has earned the accolade of "most polluted" today, it is surely the Arthur Kill, an 11-mile-long, narrow stretch of saline water dividing New Jersey from the western shore of Staten Island. Arthur Kill (its name is derived from *kil,* an old Dutch word for channel or creek) has on its shores, among other things, the largest oil storage center on the east coast. Though it flows directly into Raritan Bay from the north, it has no aquatic life at all, has a dissolved oxygen reading of zero even in the winter (which is considered quite extraordinary by sanitation engineers), and is officially classified as a sewer. A survey completed in 1958 by the Interstate Sanitation Commission reported that there was a giant slug of pollution 6.4 miles in length, "moving to and fro with the ebb and flood of the tide," in Arthur Kill, apparently forever trapped there, like a monster in some hideous primeval fen.

In fact, the prospect of Arthur Kill and its industry-clogged shores, as one sees them from the Goethals Bridge linking Staten Island with New Jersey, readily induces such mournful speculation. It is a nightmare world uncomfortably close to that through which Little Nell and her grandfather passed on their flight from the Old Curiosity Shop: "On every side, and as far as the eye could see into the heavy distance, tall chimneys, crowding on each other, and presenting that endless repetition of the same dull, ugly form, which is the horror of oppressive dreams, poured out their plague of smoke, obscured the light, and made foul the melancholy air." Dickens would have relished Arthur Kill.

The Public Health Service set up at the Raritan Arsenal what has become a semi-permanent headquarters for its study. Project Director Paul DeFalco heads a staff of 30 people, about half of them scientists, operating on a federal budget of $250,000 a year. The program has included semi-annual conferences with officials of the concerned states to determine what progress has been made, and continuing studies of the contaminated water by PHS scientists. Dyes and tracers added to the currents and tides proved "that water, and incidentally pollution, entering the Bay at almost any point ultimately may travel to almost all other points in the Bay." At one of the PHS conferences, Mrs. Norma Cirella, a Staten Island resident, testified somewhat excitedly to what scientists had expressed about the bay in a different manner.

"You read the papers and all you hear is figures and statistics and whatnot," she told the experts. "That water is so polluted I wouldn't put a dead dog in it."

Public Health Service investigators found that the bay's primary problem was the raw sewage poured into it from bordering municipalities. The area was a giant cesspool. Tottenville, an industrial community of 9,000 people on Staten Island, poured its sewage and industrial wastes untreated into Raritan Bay. The Rahway Valley Sewerage Authority alone was dumping 22.5 million gallons of sewage a day into Arthur Kill after "treating" it in a plant designed for only 16.7 million gallons. In all it was estimated that the sewage of 500,000 people was discharged, inadequately treated, into Arthur Kill. Vast amounts of filth from the sewers of Manhattan and Brooklyn were washed through the Narrows and into the Raritan Bay area. The record teemed with reports of minor infiltrations: "Lemon Creek (on Staten Island) is the only sizable stream flowing into the bay from this area. Its fresh water contribution is small, but polluted. The other small drainage streams carry some incidental pollution from cesspools in the local area." Alongside the names of townships and industries contributing to the pollution were those of obscure institutions—the Mount Loretto Home (with 1,000 children and 200 adults), the Marist Novitiate, Richmond Memorial Hospital, and St. Joseph's Home on Staten Island—contributing their small, but in the end significant, share.

Pollution emptied into the bay did not leave quickly. It was found that sewage overflowing into Raritan Bay from Arthur Kill took two weeks to find its way to the Atlantic Ocean. Sludge deposits from some sewage-treatment plants were barged out to sea and dumped there, but dumpings were often delayed by foul weather and labor disputes. The most obvious evidence of pollution in the bay was the high coliform bacteria count. A PHS report issued in 1963, two years after the study began, reported "high orders of fecal coliforms and fecal streptococcus" encountered in the western part of Raritan Bay. "The sanitary significance of the presence of organisms, known to be from feces of warm-blooded animals and humans, is that this represents actual pollution of these waters either by untreated or inadequately treated sewage." Another PHS report said that "the waters of the beaches along both the upper and lower ends of Staten Island's southeastern shore, and along the New Jersey shore in the vicinity of the mouth of the Raritan River and the southern end of Arthur Kill, have bacterial contamination in excess of that considered safe for bathing. The offshore waters of these same areas present a health hazard to those who use them for boating, skiing, or fishing." It called the waters of Arthur Kill "potentially hazardous to the health of those who use it for any purpose that might permit ingestion of even small quantities of the water."

The problem is especially acute in the summer when vacationers flock to beach resorts, overloading the capacities of local sewage-treatment plants. A PHS report said that the discharge from a sewage-treatment plant in Perth Amboy, New Jersey, "deserves special comment. This effluent discharges about 200 feet offshore at approximately the center of the bathing area of a Perth Amboy public bathing beach. The resulting boil is readily apparent from the beach." The report mentioned both a high coliform bacteria count and "suspended solids." But Perth Amboy bathers are not frolicking in filth that is solely their own. Only a mile across the water is a Tottenville, Staten Island, outfall which discharges 400,000 gallons of sewage each day in the direction of Perth Amboy beaches. After a tour of the area a couple of years ago, New Jersey

State Senator Nelson A. Stamler referred to Perth Amboy's playground as "Bacteria Beach."

Though only 35 of New York City's 575 miles of coastline are officially considered safe for swimming, there is considerable doubt about the safety of even that limited area. A bulletin issued on June 23, 1961, by the Commanding Officer of Fort Wadsworth on Staten Island, declared the beaches "off-limits" to his troops. The order read in part: "Because of the great variance in bacteriological standards for salt water swimming areas acceptable to local health authorities and the Army Medical Service, all personnel assigned, attached, or living on this installation have been urged through Post published media to refrain from swimming at all beaches on Staten Island even though rated Class A by local authorities."

But industrial waste, as any dismayed observer of the scene at Arthur Kill will testify, plays its part in the pollution of Raritan Bay. While municipal pollution is chiefly a product of the local citizens' sloth, industrial pollution is very often a product of the businessman's untenable claim that sewage disposal is a legitimate use of water (just as the millinery trade once claimed that birds were created to provide plumes for the hats of fashionable women). Following the Public Health Service's detailed description of the pollution it had discovered in the vicinity of Raritan Bay in 1961, Dr. Mitchell Wendell, Counsel for the Interstate Sanitation Commission, challenged the conservation point of view.

"There is no inference, or, you would not contend, would you, that waste disposal is not one of the very legitimate and normal uses of bodies of water? That may make other uses inappropriate, or it may be you would prefer not to use it for waste disposal, but waste disposal is one such purpose, isn't it?"

To which Harold F. Clark, a PHS bacteriologist, replied: "I do not consider waste disposal such a purpose unless the waste is adequately treated and will not interfere with the other legitimate water uses it should be put to."

When the PHS began to look into the Raritan Bay problem, there was very little known about the contributing industrial pollution. Each industry might admit that there *was* pollution, but would contend that certainly its own insignificant load wasn't doing the damage. A 1963 report by Humble Oil Company, before the House Committee on Government Operations, phrased it this way: "We have recently been informed by the State of New Jersey that further reduction of organic wastes in the Bayway effluent will be necessary because of the undesirable situation existing in the Arthur Kill. Although the refinery effluent quality is such that it would normally present no problems in the Kill by itself, it is not satisfactory to meet today's requirements when added to the existing BOD load [a measure of the bio-degradable organic material present] from nearby communities and industries."

In 1965, four years after PHS's entry into the area, Ian McNett of the Perth Amboy *Evening News* wrote the comprehensive sort of series about local water pollution problems that might benefit every community. The series emphasized the many delays which frustrate an orderly solution to our water problems. Though New Jersey had issued orders to a dozen industries in 1963 demanding that they clean up their wastes, McNett reported that none had complied with the orders by 1965. Mentioning specific names, McNett said that the Philip Carey Manufacturing Company on the Raritan River in Perth Amboy had been ordered by the State Health Department to stop polluting the water in 1961. "It gave the company another warning last summer and turned the case over to the State Attorney General. So far no determination of the case has been made," McNett wrote.

According to McNett, the Bakelite Division of the Union Carbide Corporation has been under state orders to clean up its waste effluent since the 1950's. At last reports, Bakelite was "studying its problems." Another New Jersey factory was cited as a source of air pollution. The factory simply turned its wastes into liquid form and is now polluting the waters. Still another New Jersey firm is presently enjoying an enviable immunity from state prosecution. Once described by a New Jersey Health Department official as the Raritan River's Number One pollution problem, the Calco Division of American Cyanamid in Bridgewater Township now goes unmolested because the state has not found its effluent to be a health problem. Its outflow pipe simply pours "a rich, coffee brown mass," smelling horribly, into the Raritan River. It is believed that some of Calco's wastes combine with the chlorine in the water to create the obnoxious brown liquid. Though nobody has yet proved this flow to be a health hazard, the State Department of Conservation and Economic Development began an investigation to find out why there aren't any fish in the river below this outfall.

"I say there should be a federal investigation!" a woman demanded at a conference conducted by the Public Health Service on Raritan Bay pollution.

"There is. Haven't you been listening?" the conference chairman said.

The lady might be forgiven, however, for being confused by the course taken by the PHS investigation. Though such a project is nominally a cooperative venture between the states and the federal government, enlisting the aid of all local segments of industry and politics, the PHS Raritan Bay project was beset by all the familiar obstacles. State jealousy, town apathy, and industrial greed merge into a morass of verbiage and detail in which eventually even a powerful federal agency flounders. The prevailing attitude here, just as in the case of the Mississippi pesticide interests, is that pollution is not a public health problem: there isn't enough contamination in the water to hurt anybody. A few ducks perish, a few fish drift to the surface and roll over and die, but the warnings go unheeded. Suddenly an epidemic breaks out, but even that doesn't cause more than a flurry of excitement. The problem is solved by putting the clammers out of business. But the viruses and virulent bacteria remain in the water. Three years after the PHS investigation began, salmonella cultures, which cause dysentery and food poisoning, were found in Raritan Bay clams (including three varieties of salmonella never before described, one of which PHS officials wanted to name *Salmonella raritana*). In an editorial written in January, 1965, the Perth Amboy *Evening News* expressed local anxiety: "In the name of public health, the beaches should be closed until the waters are cleaned up."

In the face of the evidence of gross pollution and the attendant public anxiety, it is inconceivable that the various state agencies involved would resent federal assistance. The attitude of New Jersey's Governor Richard J. Hughes, as he expressed it before a Senate sub-committee in 1963, indicated that PHS aid would be welcomed. "We in New Jersey want to avoid any doctrinaire position on States' Rights—for or against—on this or any other issue," Hughes said. "Where we possess the ability and the resources and the will to best provide needed services, we want to do the job ourselves. Where the special resources—financial and otherwise—of the Federal Government can do the job better, and perhaps faster, we are not too proud to seek Federal support."

The states obviously were not equipped to handle the gigantic problems posed by Raritan Bay. Yet throughout the PHS conferences, state officials bristled with that defensive air peculiar to bureaucrats who feel that someone is "pulling rank" on them. William C. Cope, chairman of the Interstate Sanitation Commission, told PHS officials that the waters of Raritan Bay were "in very good condition for virtually every use that can be made of them, including those uses requiring a high degree of purity such as fishing and bathing . . . Even the fate of the Raritan Bay shellfish beds hardly presents the 'national interest' that would justify enforcement action by the Public Health Service."

Since there is no record of Chairman Cope having been detected swimming off "Bacteria Beach," some comment on his statement may be justified. Murray Stein, of the PHS Enforcement Branch, confined himself to a quotation from the Federal Water Pollution Control Act, empowering the government to act when apparent pollution in one state endangers the public health in another. He juxtaposed this quotation with those detailing the hepatitis epidemic and the analysis of waters in which people swam, boated, skied, and fished. "I think the Surgeon General under the law was doing his duty," Stein said.

(At that time the Surgeon General, rather than the Secretary of HEW, sent the Public Health Service into a pollution case.)

When Stein, contesting the amount of "progress" claimed by the states in clearing up the pollution, said that one of PHS's hardest jobs was "terminating a case and getting out," Dr. Mitchell Wendell, the Interstate Sanitation Commission's Counsel interrupted to say, "We are offering you the opportunity to do just that."

"I suspect, Dr. Wendell," Stein replied, "that you would have offered this opportunity before we called the conference."

Repeatedly, officials from the states and the Interstate Sanitation Commission reminded conference audiences that they had "not requested help" from the Public Health Service. After listening to the well-documented summaries of the pollution presented by PHS scientists, the states' summaries consisted chiefly of invitations to Stein to close the conference. Perhaps one explanation of this extraordinary attitude displayed by state officials may be found in the testimony of Dr. Hollis S. Ingraham, New York State's Commissioner of Health, before the Committee on Government Operations in 1963. Asked by the committee counsel if he knew of any instances where the federal government had usurped the states' prerogatives, Ingraham replied, "The only instance I have is in this Raritan Bay thing where we felt that this was something that should have been done by informal consultation rather than open hearings."

It is obvious that state officials assume federal interference to be an attack on their professional reputations. "It looks like a reflection on the job they're doing," a PHS investigator says. "And frankly, it is."

Municipalities have proven to be another obstacle to cleaning up Raritan Bay. The problem throughout the area today is not that there is no sewage treatment at all, but that so much of it is inadequate. According to the records of the Interstate Sanitation Commission, which investigates sewage-treatment plants in the area, many of the plants do not meet the minimum requirements set by the commission for the removal of suspended solids and coliform bacteria in their effluents. Other municipalities have tried to keep up with the schedule set for them by various state agencies, or by court orders. The Middlesex County Sewerage Authority spent $32 million to build a trunk sewer and a treatment plant, and will spend an additional $20 million to improve older facilities. On the other hand, Ian McNett in the Perth Amboy *Evening News* reported in 1965 that Carteret, New Jersey, was not keeping up with the timetable assigned to it. A local councilman, according to McNett, said that the "borough would not spend its own money for the plant, but was applying instead for federal funds." Yet the state health department doubted that Carteret would be able to obtain the federal funds in time to keep up with its schedule.

While industry pollution in the entire area is still overshadowed by that of municipal sewage, the "hard-headed" but frequently sanctimonious attitude of many industrial leaders may be more difficult to combat than the less articulate resistance of state and municipal leaders. This attitude, as expressed by a state official especially tolerant of industrial wastes, goes something like this: "I don't think that we in our economy must require wastes to be treated beyond the point at which the stream will absorb those wastes. My own concept of this industrial question is not how much should we make industry do but how little is necessary for industry to do in the way of waste treatment and still maintain the water in the outlet stream for the legitimate uses of that stream below that outlet."

Frank Gregg, a distinguished conservationist, has pointed out the fallacy in this kind of reasoning. "I would say that certainly we should use streams for the full assimilative capacity that they have for absorbing waste," Gregg says. "But I am quite certain that I would not define 'full' in exactly the same way that I might if I operated a pulp mill, for instance. If we begin by saying that we are going to use waters to the maximum capacity for waste treatment, we will maintain them at a level which is just above that required to keep from killing each other, but we certainly won't be taking advantage of the waters' capacity to serve the widest range of human uses, including recreation."

The peak of sanctimoniousness in this area was attained perhaps by the industrialist who claimed that water is polluted by factory wastes "because of the American's demand for a high standard of living." The ultimate plea by a besieged polluter is that the authorities must go easy on him because he might be forced to close down his business; in other words, "don't throw out the baby with the dirty bath water." Murray Stein replies that "we haven't put anybody out of business yet."

The conference on Raritan Bay brought out the fact that there already has been some progress made toward cleaning up the waters, and the intervention by PHS has stimulated more. The cost of sewage-treatment-plant construction in New Jersey has risen spectacularly. In the ten-year period between 1929 and 1938 there was $57 million spent in the state for municipal sewers and treatment plants. During the wartime years (1939-48) the ten-year cost dropped to $49 million, creating untold pollution problems. Struggling to catch up, New Jersey spent $275 million in the next ten years (1949-58) and $235 million in the next *five* years (1959-63). It is estimated that $700 million will be spent in the state in the next ten years. No one knows what the cost to industry will be if it decides unanimously to play its part in the purifying of nearby waters. When asked at the conference what steps the Interstate Sanitation Commission had taken to see that industry cut down on its heavy pollution load, the commission chairman replied:

"In some cases you notify the operator to see if he can control it. In some cases—in extreme cases—in two or three cases, where it failed, they got these court orders against them now. So action is being taken on all those cases. But it varies with each case on how you handle it."

There is an occasional reward for the persevering citizen who sits through the pollution conferences, or who reads their transcripts. Such was the case during the conference held at New York City in May, 1963. The conference had taken on a cloyingly unreal air as state officials read windy statements explaining how they had the situation under control. ("We are convinced that a healthy situation of progress exists," a man from the New York State Conservation Department said. Dr. Hollis S. Ingraham, New York State's Commissioner of Health, said that the Public Health Service study had only confirmed "much of what has already been known concerning these problems." He suggested that the PHS retire from the scene and leave the problem to the state agencies. "Any other course of action would be distasteful to these various agencies which have demonstrated that they are competent to carry out their presently operative and planned progress.") Was this Raritan Bay they were talking about? People who had observed the bay, and occasionally smelled it, wondered. Then Charles Callison of the National Audubon Society was called on to make a statement.

"It is my strong belief," Callison said, "based on reports of the polluted condition of the waters of Raritan Bay that have appeared in the press, and which have been reported here and elsewhere, that the problem is such a colossal one that only a small beginning, at best, has been made in actual abatement. I question that anyone here really knows or is in a position yet to know if there has been any measurable improvement in the heavily polluted parts of Raritan Bay.

"The United States Public Health Service cannot escape its responsibility in this area, despite the invitation heard today for them to get out. In my opinion the state and interstate agencies should welcome the help of the federal government. It came as a little bit of, not a little shock, but a tremendous shock, to me to hear the defensive and negative statements that were presented by the New Jersey and New York authorities today.

"Thank you."

A burst of applause, for the first time, shattered the self-satisfied air of the conference room.

Yet even the success of the Public Health Service in this

project has been questioned. Congressman John D. Dingell has said that PHS not only failed to abate the pollution but didn't even carry out its responsibilities in interstate quarantine by banning the taking of shellfish long before disaster struck. Speaking of the Raritan Bay Conference, Dingell said, "Frankly, it is my opinion that it occurred under circumstances which looked to me like a whitewash."

The New Republic was similarly critical of what it called a "pollution boggle" at Raritan Bay. "Both New York and New Jersey have been studying pollution in this cesspool since 1955," it said in the fall of 1964. "The Federal government intruded in 1961, after enough people came down with hepatitis. It conducted a study, and there were promises all around that the bay would be cleaned up. Now, there is yet another study. That makes nine years of studying. The point of this particular research is to discover the direction and force of the current in and out of various parts of the bay and surrounding creeks. A small boy in a rowboat could determine this."

In the swirl of charge and counter-charge the plight of the ruined clammers has been all but overlooked. Elizabeth M. Wallace, Director of the Oyster Institute of America, has pointed out that Raritan Bay remains a menace to the entire shellfish industry. The possibility that "black-market" clammers may take diseased clams from the bay must haunt both clammers and health officials. "As long as these resources cannot be used," Mrs. Wallace said, "they are as a pistol to the heads of our whole industry, because should these shellfish be taken and get to the markets, it destroys the industry all over our country."

Martin Feldman, a New Jersey clammer, expressed to

the conferees the attitude of his fellow workers. "Everyone was thrown out of work," he said. "We would like to know when these men will be able to go back to work, or is it going to be caught in government bureaucracy and go on for 10, 15, or 20 years."

"I think in a year, when the study is completed," Murray Stein said, "we will be in a much better position at least to give you a prognosis, or to say after the study, we don't know and we can't tell you."

"That's all we been hearing," Feldman said.

Today, a couple of years later, the answer seems to be a gloomy one. "Even when and if every town and industry puts in effective treatment plants," a PHS official says, "we will still have the problem of stormwater overflow. In rainy weather, the sewage flow will be just too much for even the most modern treatment plants, and the bulk of it, solids and all, will be bypassed directly to the bay. That means the clams will be subject even then to intermittent pollution."

A state official has this to say. "Certainly it will be possible to effect improvements, but whether or not these will be sufficient to permit reopening of certain areas of the bay to shellfishing is a question. Shellfish beds located so close to a great metropolitan complex, such as that of the New York City area, present a unique problem that in all of its aspects, from a practical and economical standpoint, may be incapable of total solution."

There is already talk of an attempt to transplant some of the clam beds to remote areas of the New Jersey and Long Island coast. The bay will be abandoned to the polluters. "Those people in Arthur Kill," says a PHS official, "will continue to wallow in their own juice."

Five: The Mississippi Fish Kill

I

On November 18, 1963, Robert LaFleur of Louisiana's Division of Water Pollution Control called the Public Health Service in Washington to report a massive fish kill in the lower Mississippi River and its tributary, the Atchafalaya. An estimated five million dead fish were floating, belly up, in the great muddy river which drains a third of the United States, provides drinking water for over a million southerners, and supports a vast segment of this country's fishing industry. LaFleur's telephone call, made reluctantly as are most pleas for help by state officials to the federal government, set in motion more than a routine investigation. Before many months had passed, roving teams of water "detectives" had touched off an uproar which was fueled by the fires from many of the basic moral, political, and business controversies of our time.

It was not the first such kill on the Mississippi in recent years. In the summer of 1958, fish, snakes, eels, and turtles died in enormous numbers in streams throughout the sugar-cane areas of southern Louisiana. State chemists could not detect toxic materials in either the water or the fish, but the carnage went on. In 1959 a state report noted that during that year's growing season "these kills reached alarming proportions with complaints being received by the Division of Water Pollution Control on an almost daily basis."

At least 30 major kills were reported during the summer of 1960. Kenneth Biglane, who was then chief of the Louisiana Water Pollution Division, recalls his department's frustration. "The sports public, indignant citizens, harassed elected officials and the press were all demanding that something be done. Dead fish were observed to be clogging the intake of the Franklin, Louisiana, power plant and were dying in Bayou Teche, a stream used as a source of drinking water for the town of Franklin."

In the fall of 1960, nearly four million fish died mysteriously in the Mississippi and the Atchafalaya. The dead fish included threadfin shad, fresh water drum, and buffalo, but by far the greatest number of victims were catfish (95 percent), the principal source of food for many of the poorer people in the river towns and bayou settlements. Although continued observation did not give scientists any clues to the cause of their death, all the dead and dying fish exhibited strikingly similar symptoms.

"Most of the catfish were bleeding about the mouth," Robert LaFleur recalls, "and many were bleeding about the fins. In every instance examination revealed that this was due to distention of the swim bladder and the digestive tract. The latter was devoid of food material and contained only gas and a small amount of bile-like frothy material. Analysis of the bottom organisms revealed that an abundant food supply was available. Dying fish were swimming at the surface, often inverted, in a very lethargic manner, and were easily captured by hand."

According to the state investigators, this was "the most spectacular fish mortality ever noted in Louisiana," but their only conclusion was that it might be attributed to "abdominal dropsy." When smaller but widespread kills occurred again in 1961 and 1962, the details were not reported to the United States Public Health Service because, according to Biglane, "We did not think pollution was responsible for the mortalities."

By 1963, however, Biglane had joined the Public Health Service in Washington, and he was among the federal pollution experts who were alarmed by the report of the massive fish kill reported that November. Louisiana officials, until then reluctant to call in the federal government on a problem which they considered rightfully belonged to the state, had thrown up their hands in despair. LaFleur's call to Washington was a plea for immediate help.

Teams of federal investigators descended on the lower Mississippi. They talked to local scientists, read reports on previous fish kills, and toured the stricken areas in small boats. There was no scarcity of evidence, and no scarcity of local people waiting to tell their stories. Harry McHugh, who lives along the Atchafalaya, told his in the Franklin *Banner-Tribune*.

"I can look out my front door," he wrote in January,

1964, "and see at least a few fish swimming crazily on the surface of the water—mostly shad and mullet. These will swim in such a fashion for a while, eventually losing their ability to swim, and then either drift on down with the tide toward the Gulf of Mexico or are washed up on the banks where they die."

A reporter for *The New Republic* learned that the streams and bayous were clogged with dead ducks, mostly fish-eating species like scaup and mergansers. "The bodies of turtles floated on the waters," *The New Republic* said. "Tough 150-pound garfish and catfish weighing 70 pounds surfaced, too weak to move. Crabs lay along the banks. Thousands of cranes and robins lay dead. The pencil-size white eels fishermen used for bait were scooped up dead by the net full. Alligators, once plentiful, have disappeared. Otter died or left the swamps."

Though many human beings lived on the product of those waters, there were no reports yet of illness and death among them. Economically, the story was different. The men who had fished the Cajun areas of Louisiana for years were hard hit. The wives of many were forced to go to work in the canneries, while the fishermen themselves took work in nearby towns or in the off-shore oil industry.

"More fishermen have gone on jobs this year than ever before," one of them told a reporter from the *New York Times*.

"This time the poison hit all types of fish," another fisherman said. "So many died this winter that it got so I couldn't make $10 a week."

A wholesaler reported that he could buy only a small percentage of the fish usually available to him. "You can stand here on the dock any day of the fall and winter and see thousands of dead fish float by with the current," he said. "They would shoot up out of the water and just flop over. Many others died in the nets before the fishermen could bring them in."

These tales were confirmed by the experience of government scientists. Dr. Donald Mount, a young biologist with the Public Health Service, told of touring the Mississippi in an open powerboat near Baton Rouge.

"Thousands of catfish, drum, buffalo and shad were seen at the surface, unable to maintain an upright position and often having convulsions. Literally acres of minnow schools were also in a state of hyperactivity and convulsions."

Dr. Mount also visited the delta areas where menhaden, a salt-water fish which enters estuaries to cast its eggs in late winter and early spring, were reported dying by the millions. Menhaden, in fact, made up by far the greatest proportion of the fish killed in the estuaries during the winter of 1963-64. Touring the harbor at Venice, 235 miles below Baton Rouge, Dr. Mount observed thousands of convulsing blue catfish, mullet, and menhaden. "On several occasions," he said, "we went into a dead-end canal, and as the boat approached the end, schools of menhaden were trapped and hundreds of these fish began convulsing, jumping onto the boat, the banks and against an oil drilling rig."

Scientists from various government agencies collected dead and dying fish, froze them, and shipped them to laboratories for study. Analysis by the U.S. Fish and Wildlife Service (Department of the Interior) proved that the fish were not killed by parasitic or bacterial disease. Botulism was ruled out, as were organic phosphorous insecticides and toxic concentrations of metals.

But government scientists were for the first time armed

with recently developed techniques and machines which brought them within reach of a solution. At the Taft Sanitary Engineering Center in Cincinnati, investigators worked for weeks to find a clue to the mysterious fish kills. Tissues of dying catfish were fed to healthy catfish, but no viral or bacterial diseases were transmitted to them. A major breakthrough resulted, however, when scientists turned to the mud which had been dredged from affected areas of the river. Extracts of the tissues taken from dying fish were then dissolved in water where healthy fish swam. The healthy fish convulsed and died—symptoms exactly similar to those of the stricken fish in the Mississippi and Atchafalaya!

Teams of investigators (one from a private research laboratory) independently analyzed both the mud and the dead fish. Endrin, a chlorinated hydrocarbon insecticide, was found in every extract.

This deadly poison was not new to government scientists. For some years the Bureau of Commercial Fisheries (Department of the Interior) had been studying Endrin and similar poisons, Dieldrin and Aldrin, because of their effect on key commercial fish like shrimp and menhaden. These insecticides, marketed because of their extreme toxicity to arthropods (the phylum to which most insect pests belong), were naturally found to be especially harmful to shrimp, which are marine arthropods. Dr. C. M. Tarzwell, chief of the Public Health Service's Aquatic Biology Section, reports that, of all the substances he ever tested, Endrin is the most toxic to fish.

Endrin, indeed, was more than a laboratory goblin. It was known to Louisiana biologists as far back as 1958, the year of the first mysterious fish kill there. They noticed then a cause-and-effect relationship between the spraying of sugar-cane fields with Endrin (to control an insect called the sugar-cane borer) and the subsequent drainage of those fields after heavy rains. Thousands of fish immediately died. When the spraying stopped, the killing stopped. Kenneth Biglane, chief of the state's Division of Water Pollution Control at the time, clearly remembers that sequence of events.

"I have witnessed aerial applications of Endrin on sugar-cane fields around Houma, Thibodaux, and Donaldsonville, Louisiana," he says. "After subsequent rains, I have returned to such streams as Bayou Pierre Part near Donaldsonville, Bayou Black near Houma, and Bayou Chevrieul near Thibodaux, and I have seen thousands of fish and snakes, turtles, eels, dead and dying."

Yet all attempts to pin down Endrin as the cause of the fish kills during those years proved futile. The advanced techniques of fish autopsy and the sensitive instruments capable of detecting minute traces of foreign substances in water and mud (as low as a few parts per billion) were not then available to investigators. The now-familiar pattern of delay began to appear. The federal government was reluctant to move in because, as one Public Health Service scientist said, "it would destroy state relations and dry up future research." State officials, jealous of their sovereignty, refused to allow federal investigators to come in and perhaps put restrictions locally on the sale of suspected pesticides. The state, of course, could have taken strong measures of its own. In 1959, Louisiana limited itself to a public education program, pointing out the dangers of the careless use of Endrin.

"Regulations for the supervision of aerial applications," Biglane says, "the marking of cane fields, the plugging of drainage ditches leading away from fields, and the halting of applications immediately before a rain was forecast were recommended to the Louisiana Stream Control Commission by our division in August, 1959. No action was taken on these recommendations."

But now, early in 1964, modern science enabled the government teams to isolate the killing substance. Dr. Donald Mount, the Ohio State graduate who had toured the lower Mississippi observing the effects of the kill and picking up dead fish, is described as one of the heroes of the investigation. Working on a new method of "fish autopsy," he was able to uncover vital evidence in the fatty tissues of his specimens. Other PHS scientists in Cincinnati, using a gas chromatograph equipped with an electron capture detector, were able to assay extracts and blood from 100 poisoned fish between December 20, 1963, and April 1, 1964. Every sample contained Endrin. When infinitesimal quantities of Endrin, corresponding to the quantities discovered by sensitive instruments in extracts of the stricken Mississippi fish, were injected in healthy fish, the latter passed through identical symptoms and died. The next problem was to discover how Endrin got into the streams and rivers.

"Endrin is not found naturally in the Mississippi River." Murray Stein has said. "The fish don't go out to a supermarket or drug store or a package store and buy it. The fish must get Endrin from their total environment."

There was one clue. Although some scientists have said for a long time that insecticides were being washed off fields into streams and rivers, Louisiana officials believed that the big fish kill of November, 1963, was not caused by field drainage. For one thing, the fields are sprayed in the spring, not in the fall. For another, most of the Louisiana sugar-cane fields are cut off from the Mississippi and Atchafalaya by levees, thereby ruling out direct drainage into them; there were no big kills in the smaller streams near the cane fields. State Sanitary Engineer John E. Trygg summed up the state's position in his report of Endrin in the river: "Although the concentrations seem to increase in reaches of the Mississippi River in Louisiana there is really no drainage to the river from Louisiana soils and there are no Louisiana industries discharging insecticide wastes into the river."

Louisiana officials concluded that the great percentage of Endrin must be entering Louisiana from another state. It was on this basis (the pollution of interstate waters) that Louisiana had requested the assistance of the federal government.

Because the Mississippi River is the United States' major inland waterway, it is also its major sewer. Countless industries adhering to the old and once-valid adage that "dilution solves all pollution," have settled on its banks primarily to have access to a natural and therefore inexpensive sewer. Though there is not a major city along the Mississippi below Minneapolis and St. Paul which has an adequate sewage-treatment plant, no one had any qualms about dumping his most noxious wastes into the great but overburdened river. In 1964 St. Louis, Memphis, Vicksburg, Natchez, and New Orleans were still pouring their raw sewage into the Mississippi. New Orleans, as well as 100 other "jurisdictions" within Louisiana, with a total population of 1,094,000, take its *drinking* water from this cloudy sewer.

"Stream scientists working for Louisiana's Division of Water Pollution Control," Kenneth Biglane says, "soon become educated to the different types of water pollution that are found in their state from time to time. Wastes from sugar factories, sweet potato canneries, pulp and paper mills, oil field brines, naval stores plants, chemical plants, municipal sewages, and slaughterhouses all have two things in common. They can degrade water and they can kill aquatic life. Their point in time, their point source, and their physical and chemical alteration of the aquatic environment, however, offer clues to their dissimilarities."

Today there are about 100,000 industries in 18 states along the Mississippi and its tributaries. Of these, 118 plants manufacture pesticides. Before the development of new techniques and instruments by PHS scientists in the last few years, it would have been nearly impossible to trace a specific poison to a specific source. Now PHS investigators set out to find the source of Endrin in the Mississippi. After talking to agricultural people who had handled Endrin, and to scientists who had observed earlier fish kills in which Endrin had been suspected, they discovered an interesting fact. The effect on fish trapped in Endrin-infested streams near sugar-cane areas immediately after spraying and heavy rains had been "acute": the fish had died immediately. The effect on most of the fish during the recent kill had been "chronic": the fish had died more slowly or, in many cases, had gone through convulsions, righted themselves, and survived. Perhaps, the scientists thought, the more recent infestation of the river was of a different nature. Perhaps the poison had been diluted, after a long passage downstream, by mingling with the enormous flow of the lower Mississippi. At Memphis, Tennessee, some 500 miles up the river, there was a plant which manufactured Endrin. PHS investigators decided to take a close look at it.

The Memphis plant was owned by the Velsicol Chemical Corporation of Chicago. Endrin itself had been developed in Velsicol's Chicago laboratories. In discussing Endrin's widespread use in the South one agronomist put it this way: "I can say without the slightest fear of being contradicted that Endrin is the most effective insecticide ever used on the Louisiana cane crop." It is effective and popular, of course, simply because it is extremely deadly: it does the job.

In April, 1964, a team of Public Health Service investigators visited the Velsicol plant at Memphis. Leading the investigators was Dr. Alfred R. Grzenda, a pesticides expert from the PHS office in Atlanta. The story of what Grzenda and his associates found in Memphis might be enlightening to those who believe industrial pollution can be cleared up merely by "education and friendly persuasion."

Grzenda's job was to gather information on the manufacture of Endrin (including its by-products) and take samples of the water and mud in the vicinity of the plant. William Anthony, Velsicol's plant manager, was apparently reluctant to give Grzenda information about the various processes involved in Endrin's manufacture. "When we asked specific questions about starting and intermediate products," Grzenda said, "Mr. Anthony referred us to the patents for the manufacture of these compounds."

According to later newspaper reports, the PHS officials

were barred from the plant, but Grzenda denied this. "We were treated well," Grzenda said, "but the Velsicol Company more or less selected the sites which we sampled. In other words, it was a guided tour through the plant."

Anthony showed Grzenda the plant's waste-treatment facility, a 50-ton lime bed used to produce a lime slurry which is added to a 40,000-gallon agitated retention tank. Anthony said that virtually no waste solids entered the tank. "However," Grzenda said, "sludge was dredged from the sides and middle of the tank and it contained a black, sticky, smelly residue. In the course of sampling, I splashed sludge on my face. It was extremely irritating to my eyes and skin."

Grzenda learned that the treatment plant was comparatively new, having been installed less than a year before (Velsicol had been manufacturing Endrin there since 1954, and discharging its wastes into nearby Cypress Creek until 1963). Asking for information on sewers in the area, Grzenda received contradictory reports from Velsicol people and city engineers about which pipes carried off trade wastes and which were city sanitary sewers. An attempt to enter one sewer was thwarted by noxious fumes; another attempt came to nothing when Grzenda discovered that smoke bombs planted in them by city officials ("to check for leaks") had made the sewers impenetrable. In all of them, including the "sanitary" sewers, Grzenda and his assistants detected strong chemical odors similar to that in the Velsicol treatment facility.

But the investigators did not have to rely on odors alone. Unexpectedly, they came across a by-pass line discharging Velsicol's trade wastes into a lake which flowed into Wolf River, a small tributary of the Mississippi. They also discovered that wastes, solid or semi-liquid, were being hauled daily from the Velsicol plant to a place called the Hollywood Dump. The wastes were carted there in caustic drums and in large containers known commercially as "Dempster Dumpsters." Shortly before the PHS men arrived, one of the workmen carting the drums to the dump had become ill when he was splashed with the wastes.

"This material is buried, or left exposed on a portion of the dump located on the flood plain of the Wolf River," Grzenda said. "All of the sites are subject to flooding. Mr. Anthony denied that any solids from the Endrin plant were being hauled to the Hollywood Dump, but we noted drums labeled 'isodrin scraps' at the dump on April 15. Isodrin is one of the compounds used in the manufacture of Endrin. However, Mr. Anthony said that such material is not normally taken to the Hollywood Dump for disposal."

Grzenda and his associates took samples of water and mud from the various sewers and dumps in the vicinity of the Velsicol plant, as well as from such small waterways as Wolf River and Cypress Creek (which he described as a "biological desert"). He found enormous quantities of Endrin and Dieldrin present. Calculating the amounts of Endrin which flowed from this area through streams and city sewers into the Mississippi, he was able to determine that about 7.2 pounds would enter the main stream in a single day, or 2,000 pounds a year. Although Endrin is marketed in a formula amounting to two percent, Grzenda made his calculations against "technical," or 100 percent, Endrin, which is 50 times stronger than the substance used on crops.

"I played with some figures that Dr. Mount gave me relative to blood volume and toxic concentration in the blood of catfish," Grzenda said, "and just playing around with a pencil, I figured if only one-*thousandth* of this amount of Endrin—that is if only two pounds a year found its way into the blood of fish, it would have the potential of killing 45 million one-pound catfish."

Grzenda, having completed his investigation, concluded that the concentration of Endrin in the water and underlying mud around Memphis exceeded by far all previous reports of concentrations of chlorinated hydrocarbon insecticides. Most of the contaminated areas were noted at sites "known to be downstream from points used or previously used by the Velsicol Chemical Corporation for waste discharge or disposal."

Soon afterward the Public Health Service made known its findings to the public. The presence of Endrin in the Mississippi had already been disclosed. This report was specific about its sources.

"Endrin discharged in the Memphis, Tennessee, area," the PHS report read, "other sources of Endrin not yet identified, and possibly other pesticides and discharges of sewage and industrial wastes of many kinds, pollute the waters of the lower Mississippi and Atchafalaya Rivers and, thereby, endanger health and welfare of persons in a State or States other than those in which such discharges originate. Such discharges are subject to abatement under the provisions of the Federal Water Pollution Control Act."

II

The Mississippi River, draining a vast area in the middle of our country, carries with it over 400 million tons of sediment a year. Reaching the sea it drops most of this sediment. Gradually the sediment, or silt, forms a delta. The 12,000-square-mile delta at the mouth of the Mississippi today has been built up over the centuries and is advancing into the Gulf of Mexico at the rate of 300 feet a year. Much of the south-central part of the United States is composed of land carried from the north and laid down by the Mississippi and its tributaries, so that the great river now flows through the land it helped to create. The river, then, is naturally discolored, but this has not always been a menace to the life it supports. On his voyage down the Mississippi, Huck Finn overheard a raftsman tell his colleagues that there was "nutritiousness in the mud, and a man that drunk Mississippi water could grow corn in his stomach if he wanted to."

Whether there is nutritiousness in the river today is open to question, but there are a great many other things in it. The Mississippi, like every other major river in the country, has been blighted for years by raw sewage. The absence of treatment facilities in most of the cities and nearly all of the river towns is a disgrace with which the people have come to live. Raw sewage is the country's leading killer of fish. It also causes various serious diseases among human beings: hepatitis, poliomyelitis, cholera. The situation, until the recent mild spasm of treatment-plant construction, had grown steadily worse on the Mississippi. The process goes on from year to year, each town taking the river water, perhaps treating it and perhaps not, then using it and turning it back to the river, which carries it just a little bit more contaminated along to the next fellow downstream. The introduction of insecticides to the river in recent years has added another, and potentially more deadly, dimension to the problem. There is a morbid little joke currently circulating among pollution experts on the Mississippi. "Pesticides can't do anything to our fish this year," it goes. "Our sewage has killed them all."

It was not a laughing matter in New Orleans when the Public Health Service released its report on Endrin in the river. Traces of Endrin were found in the drinking water of that big river city, as well as in the water of Vicksburg. (Purification systems for drinking water cannot remove Endrin.) New Orleans citizens who could afford it took in supplies of bottled water. Only a few hours after the PHS announcement, one New Orleans bottled-water dealer announced that he was placing customers on a five-month waiting list for his product. The uproar continued throughout April. James M. Quigley, Assistant Secretary of Health, Education and Welfare, said that after looking over the evidence he would not care to eat a Gulf shrimp cocktail. Dr. James M. Hundley, Assistant Surgeon General, on the other hand, said that he didn't feel there was any present danger involved in drinking Mississippi water or eating Gulf shrimp, but he added that he did not think it healthy to try to subsist exclusively on a diet of Mississippi catfish. The Food and Drug Administration discovered an interstate shipment of canned oysters containing traces of Endrin, but did not seize it on the grounds that it was not considered "an imminent danger to health." The government decided to survey the entire season's harvest before deciding what to do with Endrin-contaminated samples. Secretary of the Interior Stewart Udall called for an immediate ban from agricultural use on long-lasting pesticides (and ordered such a ban throughout the 550 million acres of public land administered by his department). The *New York Times,* in an editorial, supported Udall's position.

"These pesticides do not break down in nature," the *Times* editorial said. "They retain their potency long after their initial use. Once put into the environment by farmers and others, these chemicals tend ultimately to enter the food chain of living creatures. There is evidence suggesting that the degree of their concentration in organisms increases as contaminated fish, for example, are eaten by birds. Since human beings complete such food chains, there is some ground for suspicion that such increasing concentration can endanger human health.

"Here is a situation," the *Times* continued, "in which the case is strong for imposition of at least some controls quickly while research goes on to accumulate more information and also to find substitute pesticides which do not pose so formidable a threat. Certainly the nation's overcapacity for food production is so great that any potential diminution of crops resulting from such pesticide restrictions would be a lesser risk than that arising from the haphazard use of the chemicals themselves."

Velsicol, under fire, shot back. Bernard Lorant, the company's vice-president in charge of research, issued strong denials. In a statement to the press, he said that Endrin had nothing to do with the Mississippi fish kill, that the symptoms of the dying fish were not those of Endrin poisoning, and that Velsicol's tests proved that the fish had died of dropsy. He went on to question the Public Health Service's accuracy in analyzing fish samples, claiming that, since Dieldrin is not a by-product of Endrin's manufacture, Dieldrin traces could not have been found at Memphis.

The row shifted from the pages of the daily newspapers to the hearing rooms of various committees investigating the fish kill. Hearings were called by both Senator Abraham Ribicoff's Sub-committee on Government Operations and the United States Department of Agriculture. Velsicol continued to question almost every aspect of the Public Health Service's case. Lorant pointed out that the amounts of Endrin in question often amounted to only a few parts per billion. He said that, of the 5,175,000 fish reported killed, five million were menhaden ("which is 96.6 percent," Lorant said, "or in the vernacular of Public Health, 966 million parts per billion"); these menhaden died in the mouth of the river, he went on, and were not collected or sampled by PHS; as there were only 175,000 others, mostly catfish, Endrin could be blamed at most in the death of 3.4 percent. He asked how Endrin could drift 500 miles down the river without causing a fish kill on the way, asked why no fish kills had been reported during 1961 and 1962, although Endrin was being manufactured and applied just as regularly, and said that it would have been impossible for Endrin to contribute to pollution in the lower Mississippi by running off the Louisiana sugarcane fields, because the fields were cut off from the river by levees.

Velsicol was supported in its arguments by the Shell Chemical Corporation, the only other manufacturer of

Endrin. According to a Shell executive, Endrin is readily sorbed into mud. "It is reassuring to realize," this official said, "that the large silt load carried by the Mississippi River acts as its own 'clean-up' agent for chlorinated or other highly absorbable pesticides."

But the Public Health Service stood its ground. One witness pointed out that the so-called infinitesimal quantities of Endrin found in certain areas (measured in parts per billion) are not quite so negligible when one considers the tremendous flow of the Mississippi. Others remarked that there was no major fish kill near Memphis because the fish in Endrin-infested waters had probably been killed off long ago ("Sometimes a sure sign of pollution abatement is a fish kill," one government investigator said. "At least it proves that there are still fish in the vicinity"). Endrin's report that the fish kill could be attributed to dropsy, and that there had been no reports of a kill in 1961 and 1962, were countered with the reminder that older methods of analysis had not been able to detect Endrin, and that earlier fish kills were not reported since they were considered due to natural causes.

In reply to Velsicol's statement that Endrin could not have reached the Mississippi from Louisiana cane fields, one PHS scientist suggested that the Endrin might come from factories where the cane was washed and treated; some of these plants border the Mississippi.

Witness after witness reflected the alarm that had invaded many sections of our government. It was noted that British authorities had already placed restrictions on three pesticides which have poisoned fish and shrimp in the United States. Dr. Clarence Cottam, a noted biologist, warned, "We're going to find human beings dying of this thing, unless we act with intelligence now." Assistant Secretary of HEW James Quigley testified, "The presence of any of these materials in any food or liquid consumed by human beings is a cause for concern, even though the levels may be far below those which might be considered an imminent health hazard."

When asked what amount of Endrin might be lethal to human beings, Assistant Surgeon General Hundley confessed to Senator Ribicoff's sub-committee that he did not know. "I don't know that an answer is available," he said.

After hearing the evidence that Endrin was present in shipments of shrimp and oysters, Senator Ribicoff commented, "There must be an awful lot of fish going into interstate commerce that should be condemned and removed from the market."

But the reply of George P. Larrick, Commissioner of the Food and Drug Administration, was guarded. "That remains to be seen," he said. "I don't want to just destroy the market for those products . . . I would prefer to wait until we have run a lot of samples. I hope we won't find massive contamination, and I don't think we will."

Ribicoff, after hearing all the testimony, came to some strong conclusions. He told the Velsicol people that they had disposed of their chemical wastes "in a primitive and dangerous manner . . . The record is overwhelmingly against your position."

Officials in the Department of Health, Education and Welfare came to similar conclusions. Until that time they had not wanted to restrict the use of dangerous pesticides, but the findings in the Mississippi River had changed their minds. "We cannot proceed in the same way in the future as in the past," Assistant Secretary Quigley testified before Ribicoff's sub-committee. He said that HEW now believed that as a "matter of prudence every possible effort should be made to control the use of the persistent pesticides in our environment."

The Department of Agriculture had also found disturbing evidence of misuse or careless handling of insecticides. Its representatives had accompanied PHS investigators to the Velsicol plant at Memphis. A USDA report confirmed that Velsicol's disposal of its wastes "is contributing substantially to the contamination of the river. It is our understanding, however, that the waste disposal system employed by this plant is in compliance with local sanitation codes."

A dispatch printed in the *New York Times* on January 17, 1965, reviewed some of the other curious circumstances in Velsicol's recent history at Memphis. "On June 3, 1963," the *Times* story said, "the Memphis Health Department reported complaints from 20 persons living near Cypress Creek, an open stream flowing through the north side of the city. Nausea, vomiting and watering eyes were the symptoms produced by gas rising from the stream. An official of the Velsicol Chemical Corporation denied responsibility. 'Endrin could not have caused the symptoms,' said Wilson Keyes, director of manufacturing.

"On June 7, 1963, 26 workmen in plants near Velsicol were taken to five hospitals after becoming ill from chlorine gas fumes. Within a year lawsuits totaling over $5 million had been filed by more than 40 persons claiming injury.

"Velsicol reacted in the first weeks of the trouble with a dinner for 150 political, civic and business leaders. 'It came as quite a shock to us to discover that there was some question about whether we were welcome in the City of Memphis,' said John Kirk, executive vice-president, down from Chicago for the event. Then Mayor Henry Loeb responded that 'this plant is very much wanted by Memphis.' His successor, William B. Ingram, Jr., took much the same position a year later."

Elsewhere along the Mississippi, Department of Agriculture investigations into pesticide plants proved to be "quite revealing." The USDA report said that "conditions were observed which appear to constitute a definite hazard. For example, it was found that a cooperage company removed material from used drums by heating and then washing them with caustic soda. Periodically, this solution is flushed into the city sanitary system. It was also found that several plants dispose of wastes at city dumps and that as a rule these dumps are located on the river side of the levee."

But the USDA, with the farmer's welfare uppermost in its reasoning, refused to take restrictive action. It confirmed the Public Health Service report that large quantities of Endrin and Dieldrin had been found in the Memphis area, but said that the river contamination had nothing to do with the agricultural use of these insecticides. It called, as usual, for further study. A Public Health Service scientist noted that the USDA, which is charged with the growth and welfare of American farming, continues to move into health research as well. "It's like getting a jewel thief to guard the jewels," he said.

The full-dress parade of all the combatants was reserved for the conference which was held on May 5-6,

1964, at New Orleans. It was called by Anthony J. Celebrezze, Secretary of Health, Education and Welfare, as a direct result of Louisiana's plea for help and the subsequent investigation by various government agencies. Present at the conference were members of these agencies, representatives of Arkansas, Tennessee, Mississippi, and Louisiana, and a number of other interested parties. Murray Stein, as usual, served as chairman. If the conference was not a complete success, at least it dramatized the obstacles to enforcing an effective program against water pollution in this country.

The Public Health Service, occasionally calling on representatives of the Department of the Interior and the Department of Agriculture, presented its lengthy case and its conclusions. Its investigators told the conferees what they had found in Memphis, and its scientists painstakingly reviewed their methods of analysis, and the results of their tests. Velsicol made its defense, and was rebutted by PHS.

Then the states and other industries took their turn before the conferees. Going over the transcript of the conference, one is impressed finally by the doggedness with which each speaker strove not so much for a final solution of this complex problem, but with defending his own position and interests. Those whose concern was with fish or other wildlife pleaded for immediate action. A representative of the Tennessee Fish and Game Commission, after describing the carnage inflicted by insecticides on the state's fish and birds, recommended that "the manufacture, distribution, and use of Endrin, Aldrin, Dieldrin, and other related chlorinated hydrocarbon pesticides be banned until the full effects of these poisons can be determined and evaluated." On the other hand, a representative of the sugar-cane growers asked the PHS to take no action, or, in a euphemistic phrase, to "undertake an extensive survey and study program to determine all the facts in this matter before a decision is made that could possibly do an injustice to agriculture in general and weaken our nation."

The tail end of that phrase struck a chord that seemed to be popular at the time with those under fire from the Public Health Service. "The great fight in the world today is between Godless Communism on the one hand and Christian Democracy on the other," Parke C. Brinkley, president of the National Agricultural Chemicals Association had said earlier that spring. "Two of the biggest battles in this war are the battle against starvation and the battle against disease. No two things make people more ripe for Communism. The most effective tool in the hands of the farmer and in the hands of the public health official as they fight these battles is pesticides."

It was a chord struck repeatedly during the New Orleans conference, as backward, Godless, pesticideless Russia was compared to a flourishing America. Another popular gambit used by Endrin's defenders was to try to make the Public Health Service ashamed of itself for doing its duty. "Until there is evidence to the contrary," a Shell Chemical official said, "it would be irresponsible for any reputable person to frighten people into believing that eating catfish or similar game fish is dangerous."

Velsicol's Bernard Lorant compared PHS's warnings to shouting "fire" in a crowded theater, then sounded aggrieved that the investigation had heaped extra work on the scientists. "None may allow unfounded, unthinking utterances that trigger a massive response of waste," he said. "In the present climate, should anyone recklessly conjecture as to hazard, hundreds of scientists initiate programs to prove or to disprove the remark. We do not always need more scientists; we frequently need less conjecture."

Representatives of the various states taking part in the conference apparently were more concerned with the ogre of "Big Government" than they were with the threat to their waterways. Though the conference was called because one sovereign state had been powerless to prevent pollution from pouring across its border, the representative of another state felt called upon to include among his recommendations to the conference a request that the federal government begin to know its place.

"It is not possible for the government in Washington to be all things to everybody," said E. H. Holeman, of the Tennessee Department of Agriculture, "and especially in the area of protecting wildlife, in preventing stream pollution, and in protecting the health and welfare of the consumer.

"The federal government will have to recognize this fact, and it is urged that they closely coordinate their consumer protection program with the state officials in order that we will have much better and more strict and a more harmonious consumer protection program."

This aggressive attitude toward Washington always carries with it a counteraction, much like the double standards of those foreign governments which encourage the stoning of our embassies and libraries one day, and ask for handouts the next. As in the present case, the most ardent States' Rightists are always quick to call for Washington's help when trouble crops up. A few minutes after Holeman had put forth this "recommendation," conference chairman Murray Stein pointed to another recommendation in which Holeman had asked for a federal standard on the limits of pesticides to be permitted in marketable foods.

"Aren't you worried about a federal standard usurping states' rights?" Stein asked him.

"Oh, no," Holeman said.

"Even though this might affect water pollution control and you would have a standard coming from Washington?"

"That wouldn't bother us. We have the same law in Tennessee, and so do 36 other states, as the Federal Food and Drug Act."

"It is very interesting to get the view of Tennessee on that," Stein commented.

At the conclusion of the conference, as Stein was trying to get the conferees to agree on a summary, the proceedings nearly bogged down in a spasm of local pride. When Stein attempted to insert a phrase saying that a certain condition "may require further study," a couple of Louisiana representatives put their backs up.

"Obviously, it is true," one of them told Stein, "but I don't like to see it there. It is an invitation for you to come back, you know. We don't think we need you on this."

"I understand," Stein said.

"We have tried not to worry you for about three years, as a matter of fact," another said.

The word *must* set off another furor. When Stein suggested the inclusion of the phrase, "known sources of Endrin must be brought under control," S. Leary Jones of the Tennessee Stream Pollution Control Board spoke up.

"I object to these *musts* coming from a federal agency," Jones said. "Make it *should* or *ought to be*."

"How about *are to be*?" Stein asked.

"We are going to clean up the stuff," Jones said, "but they can't tell us what we *must* do."

"The thing is this," Louisiana's Robert LaFleur, who had made the original telephone call to Washington, interrupted. "If we are going to suffer from this next fall, I am going to be boxed into a corner, and I don't want that."

"This won't happen, I guarantee," Jones said. "But a *must* in there is just one of these words that I won't agree to."

"I sure want it to be cleaned up," LaFleur said.

"All I can tell you, Bob, is that if we say *should* it has no force and effect," chairman Stein reminded him.

"It doesn't have any force or effect either way, until you go into a hearing and into federal court," Jones said. "You know that."

"Most of these cases have been solved by conference," Stein reminded him.

"This isn't a case. This is a conference."

"When I speak of case I am using a generic term," Stein said.

"All right," Jones said. "Put *should* there."

"If that man will promise me he is going to clean it up," LaFleur nodded, "I will buy his *should*."

And so the conference sputtered to a close. Endrin, originating at Memphis, was concluded to have been a contributing factor to the previous fall's kill of Mississippi catfish, and all parties were urged to see that it did not happen again. Yet, though the government's finest scientists, equipped with the most modern machines and techniques, had come to a definite conclusion about the source and agent of the fish kill, the uproar continued. Velsicol went on maintaining its (and Endrin's) complete innocence. *Chemical Week,* a trade publication, called the conference "a kangaroo court." And, on the floor of the United States Senate, Republican leader Everett McKinley Dirksen rose to attack the United States Public Health Service, claiming it had made "wild accusations" and had "unjustly crucified" Velsicol before it had all the facts. Dirksen's tirade surprised nobody. The Illinois Senator has been for a long time the champion in Congress of the nation's drug and chemical companies, as anyone can testify who recalls his bitter opposition to the Kefauver drug bill a few years earlier.

There were expressions of dismay in the press and among public health and conservation groups when Velsicol persisted in its unregenerate stance. On the other hand Murray Stein, a man of few illusions, speaks of the case today with some satisfaction. "A lot of the criticism from the chemical people was directed at me personally," Stein says with a delighted grin. "They made a big man out of me and I got some offers for important jobs. More important, though, in many aspects this was the easiest case we've ever had. It was open and shut, and our tests show that the river around there is a lot cleaner since we went after those people."

In 1965 a few fish died in the upper cane brakes after Endrin had run off the fields in the spring, but there was no slaughter on the scale of previous years. At Memphis,

PHS investigators looked into a city sewer, however, and found it caked with deposits of Endrin sludge nearly three feet thick. It was estimated that 8,000 pounds of Endrin were embedded along a 3,400-foot stretch of sewer. City officials hastily closed it off and built a bypass sewer.

"The stuff is still in the sewer," Stein says. "And it will probably stay there for a while. Who would go in there after it?"

Six: The Great Lakes and the Great Debate

I

"This huge lake is already well on the way toward becoming a shallow dishpan of soiled water, incapable of supporting any marine life that is not too loathsome to live in sludge."

The speaker was Senator Philip A. Hart of Michigan, and his subject the condition of Lake Erie. One of the five Great Lakes, Erie is "dying:" it is slowly being filled in from its center by a relentless influx of natural and man-made pollutants. This process, called "eutrophication" by scientists, is not uncommon. Lakes, like human beings, have a life cycle and proceed from youth to maturity to death. Every lake, even those in past geologic time before man arrived to speed up the process, gradually fills with silt carried into it by rivers and land runoff, as well as with the decayed remains of the plant and animal life which grow within it. Until now, scientists have considered this process to be irreversible. Suddenly we are confronted by two remarkable developments in the story of the Great Lakes. A few people, on the one hand, believing that Lake Erie's death may be averted, are working intensively to reverse the supposedly-irreversible process. A great many people, on the other hand, are continuing to burden not only Lake Erie, but the four other Great Lakes, with human and industrial wastes which, unchecked, might ultimately destroy the largest single supply of fresh water possessed by mankind.

Nearly 20 million people, or almost ten percent of the population of the United States, live in counties bordering the Great Lakes. Many of them take their drinking water from the lakes, others find their livelihood or recreation there. Yet in 1964 a Wisconsin survey found that 27 cities drawing their drinking water from Lake Michigan "face a potential health hazard from polluted lake waters." Senator Hart called water pollution "the most serious threat to Michigan's economic future." Dr. J. L. McHugh of the Bureau of Commercial Fisheries has described the decline of commercial and game fish in Lake Erie, and their replacement by "trash" fish better adapted to their polluted environment.

"It really seems incredible," Dr. McHugh said, "that one of the largest lakes in the world could already be very seriously affected by pollution, but it is. The basin in the western end has undergone a complete change in bottom life during the last 30 years or so. Our studies have shown that sludge-worms, a sure indicator of pollution, have multiplied enormously, and the larvae of insects such as mayflies, which are important as fish food, have virtually disappeared. The valuable traditional fishery resources have almost disappeared also, and other less desirable fishes have multiplied to take their place."

Inland cities send partially treated sewage toward the Great Lakes, as Syracuse does toward Lake Ontario along the Oswego River. Beaches have been closed at Cleveland, Buffalo, Milwaukee, and other cities along the lakes as the wastes they disgorge wash back against their shores. According to Stan Spisiak of the New York State Conservation Council, "Beaches along the entire shore line of Lake Erie are being closed down by local health authorities because of gross pollution. Worst of all, many local health authorities, because of a false pride and a misplaced loyalty, as well as financial consideration, are permitting beaches to remain open which should be closed."

The lakes were, and are, afflicted by a variety of ills, many of them in addition to the absence or scarcity of sewage-treatment plants common to most rivers. Cleveland, for instance, suffers despite its "adequate" treatment facilities. A considerable amount of sewage, it was revealed in 1964, never reaches the treatment plants because of leaks in its sewer pipes. "Leaks and runoffs mean that untreated wastes get to Lake Erie shore water," a local engineer explained. The Ohio Water Pollution Control Board found Cleveland's $6.7 million construction program inadequate to repair the damage. Elsewhere, harassed city officials pointed an accusing finger at the Canadian border. A Detroit official testified before a congressional committee that Canada might be adding pollution to Lake Huron. "There is some suspicion on our part —and I want to leave it in that category, and I am not saying anything here that I haven't said other places—

there is a suspicion on our part that the periodic dumping of wastes that have been lagooned up there are the ones that are coming down in slugs and creating our problems. I believe from our standpoint—from my standpoint, representing the job I do—it is very difficult for me to ask our city fathers to appropriate funds, or to ask any agency for more funds, when they know there isn't too much being done on the other side."

One of the stickier problems on the Great Lakes is the increasing pollution from ships. The St. Lawrence Seaway has opened the lakes to 90 percent of the world's commercial vessels. According to a statement by James Quigley, Assistant secretary of HEW, "Few ships afloat today, even those of recent design, have any facilities for the collection, treatment, or disposal of shipboard wastes. Laws and harbor regulations are very difficult to enforce. Bilges can be pumped out at night and many ship's captains do not honor the ten-mile limit in this regard. Accidents and carelessness in handling cargoes can happen at any time . . . The discharge of shipboard sewage near public water supply intakes is of special concern since many of these intakes are in or near present port areas. With ships from all parts of the world entering and harboring in waters adjacent to public water supply intakes, the chances are greatly enhanced for water-borne disease transmission, and particularly those diseases from other countries which have long been gone from the American scene or never have gotten a foothold here. Ships taking on fresh water from the Great Lakes run the same risk, particularly if by chance they are in the same lane with other ships that are discharging or have discharged sewage."

That they have created a sewer in their front yards is

evident to residents of lakeside cities. A man whose home is along Lake Erie's shore at Euclid, Ohio, recently said that he sees technicolor effects in the lake waters. There are blues, oranges, and blacks, and one milky white mass which took several hours to pass his home he described as "the worst example of pollution I've seen here in ten years." Euclid's mayor acknowledged the problem, and said he was trying to trace the source of this contamination. In the fall of 1963 and again in the fall of 1964, more than 10,000 gulls and loons were found dead on the shore of Lake Michigan. Scientists were not able to isolate the cause of their deaths, but noted that traces of insecticides were found in water samples taken in the area where the dead birds had piled up.

Not everyone, it must be admitted, is worried. In the spring of 1965 a dissident Milwaukeean set out to prove that his city's Grant Park Beach, closed since 1958 because of pollution, should be reopened. Once a week, "until time eternal," he said, he would wade into the waters off the beach, scoop up a sample of the water, and drink it. When last heard of, still hale and hearty, he was insisting the water was "delicious." A Public Health Service official wished him luck.

More concrete steps to open Great Lakes' beaches are being taken today by PHS scientists. Lake Erie is one object of their attention. Every major river flowing into the lake is grossly polluted. Sewage, partly treated or not at all, rushes in from countless outfalls. Compounding the problem are infinite varieties of nutrients in the sewage and runoff which stimulate the growth of algae (or green scum). Living algae, gathered in great quantities near the surface, suck so much oxygen into the water that fish choke on it; dying, the algae use up oxygen during the process of decay and create a kind of "vacuum" around them as they drift to the bottom of the lake. Reaching bottom, the decayed remnants build up the lake's floor, already littered with silt and the remains of other plant and animal life. It is this enormous floor litter which is filling the lake and which, unless checked, will create first a bog and then dry land.

Public Health Service scientists hope to prevent the lake's destruction by cleaning up the water. The first, and traditional, step is to see that every drop of waste water returning to the lake is adequately treated. The second, and unconventional, step is to try to remove the nutrients (chiefly phosphorous) that stimulate the flourishing growth of algae. To "sweep" the lake clean of its algae would be one of the greatest engineering feats of all time, yet PHS scientists feel that the effort to save Lake Erie is worth it.

"We can't think of anyone outside the agency who agrees with us," a PHS official says. "It's fair to say that we stand alone in believing that it can be done. We'll have to prove our case."

II

If the solution to Lake Michigan's problem is not as "far out," its mechanics are of more immediate interest to the general public. Lake Michigan dangles like a long bag from the 1,160-mile stretch of Great Lakes (it is the only one lying entirely within the boundaries of the United States), and its southern end is a vast *cul de sac*. About this end of the lake are clustered the great population and industrial centers of Chicago and its Indiana neighbors. Since 1840, Chicago has taken its drinking water from the lake. The city expanded at a breathtaking rate in the latter half of the 19th century, leading many people (especially civic-minded Chicagoans) to believe it was destined to become the world's greatest city. Before long its industries, especially the meat-packing houses, were recognized as a menace to the city's water supply. In the 1860's a Chicago newspaper confronted the problem as foolishly as influential people in other cities did in later times. "We believe we cannot afford to banish the industrial establishments from which issue the principal streams of impurity," an editorial assured its worried readers. "We think the city can better afford to bring its drinking water from Evanston than to drive the packing houses to St. Louis."

The city fathers apparently agreed, and the result was disease. A particularly devastating typhoid fever epidemic struck Chicago in 1891, killing more than 2,000 people. It was at this time that engineers performed a feat which must give confidence today to those who believe it is possible to save Lake Erie. They dug the famous Chicago Sanitary and Ship Canal, reversing the flow of the Chicago River, which formerly had flowed into Lake Michigan. The city simply dumped its sewage into the canal and it was carried by way of the Chicago, Des Plaines, and Illinois Rivers toward a junction with the Mississippi. This striking feat in a sense fulfilled LaSalle's glorious dream of linking the Great Lakes with the "great river." It also properly outraged the people of St. Louis and other Mississippi towns, who were now faced with the prospect of having their source of water supply inundated by Chicago's sewage. But Chicago had, temporarily, solved its problem: prizing prevention above cure, it had effectively separated its massive and deadly sewage from its drinking water.

In recent years this revolutionary project has brought Chicago a number of problems. Most urgent is the condition of the Sanitary Canal itself. Chicago's expanding population and industry have overburdened the canal (now commonly called the Illinois Waterway) with their wastes. A PHS report says that "on the basis of every criterion commonly used to judge the effects of sewage on water quality, the waterway is seriously degraded throughout the Metropolitan Area, and for many miles downstream."

Chicago, in a very real sense then, wallows in its own filth. As the PHS report goes on to say, "The pollution pattern of the Illinois Waterway differs in one important aspect from the pattern in the majority of polluted streams of the nation. In such situations, the municipality or industry causing the pollution suffers little or no damage from its own wastes. Downstream communities and other water users bear most of the burden of damages . . . Most of the worst effects of pollution appear in the waterway as it flows through the heart of this city of five and one-half million people."

In an attempt to dilute its damaging sewage Chicago has tapped Lake Michigan for enormous quantities of water. Originally it took a billion gallons a day into the Illinois Waterway to float both boats and sewage downstream. More recently it took another billion gallons to flush away its increasingly sluggish wastes. The people of other states bordering the Great Lakes protested bitterly, claiming that Chicago was "stealing" water that rightfully belonged to all of them in common. To cope with its present wastes Chicago needs an additional 650 million gallons.

Chicago fights on almost alone. New York State, for instance, claims that Chicago is appropriating water which New York uses for hydroelectric power at Niagara Falls. Wisconsin claims that Chicago is lowering the lake's level and drying up important wildlife-breeding swamps and other recreation areas. Other states complain that Chicago, by reducing the lake's water level, alters the draft of ships and so drastically affects the amount of commercial tonnage carried on the Great Lakes over the course of a year.

Despite its long fight to keep separate its sewage and drinking water, and despite the excellent purifying facilities it has built, Chicago's source of drinking and recreational water has been threatened for some time. The very states which demand that Chicago return its effluent to Lake Michigan have returned their own and thereby polluted the lake. Many of these states have had to close their own beaches. Because the southern end of Lake Michigan is a *cul de sac,* the pollution there has no outlet. Public Health Service Studies have shown that the sewage simply eddies about offshore, threatening to convert the entire area into an enormous cesspool. Municipal sewage and industrial wastes from neighboring Indiana today drift into Chicago's offshore waters. The five million people in the Chicago area who take their drinking water from Lake Michigan are exposed to increasingly high counts of coliform bacteria.

"This type of pollution," says Dr. Samuel Andelman, Chicago's Health Commissioner, "carries with it the threat of outbreaks of infectious hepatitis, typhoid fever, salmonellosis (a severe bowel infection), and possibly poliomyelitis. At present water used for drinking purposes is being maintained safely. But persons using the lake for swimming and other recreational purposes do not have the protection of filtration and chlorination."

Chicago's predicament is not new. Many of the industries polluting the lake today were accused of threatening Chicago's water supply in 1944. Chicago filed suit in the Illinois Supreme Court and received a consent decree under which the polluters were ordered to correct their abuses. Nothing happened. Late in the 1940's Chicago was forced to close some of its beaches. In his book, *The Second City* (1952), A. J. Liebling spoke of those Gold Coast apartment buildings along Lake Shore Drive from which the chlorine taste of ordinary Chicago tap water had been filtered. "This service costs two dollars a month per apartment," Liebling wrote, "and is a more satisfactory solution of the taste problem from a Gold Coast point of view than having the city bring palatable water from afar for everybody, which would mean higher taxes."

The Public Health Service became seriously interested in the affair around 1960 when the squabble between Chicago and the assembled Great Lakes states grew more complex. The U.S. Supreme Court turned the case over to a federal judge in Philadelphia, who will hear volumes of testimony before rendering a decision (which has yet to be given). While preparing testimony for this case the PHS made a survey of the southern end of Lake Michigan. It recommended to the court that Chicago be permitted to continue drawing water from the lake and diverting it to the Illinois waterway. It concluded that if Chicago were to return its effluent to the lake, as the other states demand, enormous islands of sludge would build up at the southern end of the lake. These masses would slowly drift on the lake's currents back toward Chicago's beaches and water intakes. To treat the effluent would not completely solve the problem. It is treated already to a high degree by Chicago's commendable sewage plants, but the treatment is said to be only about 89 percent effective. Untreated industrial wastes, stormwater overflow and other sources allow raw sewage to enter the water. PHS officials estimate that the Chicago area discharges, including its municipal and industrial sewage, an effluent equivalent to the wastes of eight million people. If the ten percent of the sewage that cannot be refined reaches the lake, it is obvious that there would be a raw effluent equivalent to a population of 800,000, or that of a city the size of Milwaukee. And Milwaukee, which does discharge its effluent to the lake, has an enormous problem, with great masses of sewage-stimulated algae, dead and decaying, clustered off its shores.

As a result of its four-year study of Lake Michigan, which proved the interstate nature of the pollution now concentrated off Chicago's beaches and water intakes, the PHS summoned Illinois and Indiana officials to a conference in March, 1965. Accustomed in the past to resentment and criticism, Murray Stein and his colleagues were pleased to note the favorable atmosphere with which the conference began in Chicago. The city was genuinely aroused by the putrid mess in which it found itself. Newspapers urged the authorities to go after the polluters. The

Chicago *American,* warning that Lake Michigan water may soon be unfit to drink, said that already "impurities have given the water at times a peculiar taste or an unpleasant odor." Chicago's *Southeast Economist* reported that "owners of room humidifiers are finding visual proof of the contamination in the form of scum and even small particles on the bottom and sides of the containers. It takes a good scrubbing with soap and scouring powder to get rid of it. Since the sediment increases in amount with increased use of the humidifier, it is obvious that we are drinking the stuff in a shockingly large amount."

Evidence poured in. The city reported that there were 64 days during 1964 when Lake Michigan, off Chicago's South Side beaches, was unfit for swimming. Authorities warned that five lakefront beaches might have to be closed in the next year or two because of "progressively increasing pollution" in the form of bacteria, and of oil and slag from the steel mills to the south. Richard Hoffmann of the Chicago *American* toured the area south of Chicago and wrote: "From the air, the dark mass looks like an ink stain on a blue blotter. It is flue dust being dumped into Lake Michigan from the United States Steel Company's south works . . . The water at the mouth of Indiana Harbor, flanked by the Youngstown Sheet and Tube Company on the north and the Inland Steel Company on the south, is a dirty bronze and looks solid enough to walk on. One observer, viewing the Indiana Harbor Canal, whose wastes flow into the lake, likened it to the River Styx, which guards the entrance to Hades."

Dr. Charles Olmstead, chief of the Department of Botany at the University of Chicago, linked air pollution to water pollution. Watching great plumes of smoke drift from Indiana out over the lake, he said, "This is another source of water pollution. You get fallout from polluted air." And the official PHS report charged, "Along the shores of Lake Michigan in Indiana and the southern shore in Illinois, the lake waters are discolored by suspended and dissolved waste materials, in sharp contrast to the pleasing appearance of the rest of Lake Michigan."

Indiana officials did not deny their responsibility. Blucher Poole of the Indiana Stream Pollution Control Board admitted his state had "not come to grips completely with the overall pollution problem." He said that Indiana was "a sizable and probably major" contributor to the pollution of Lake Michigan. Just as gratifying to the federal enforcement officials was the about-face performed by Chicago's Mayor Richard J. Daley. In 1963 Daley had told a House committee that Chicago and other local areas should be allowed to solve their own water pollution problems by cooperating with neighboring localities. Now, in 1965, he told the PHS conference it was "apparent that cooperation alone is not sufficient to to meet the critical threat." Murray Stein later said he had "waited 20 years" to hear such vigorous support of proper enforcement action.

The PHS report offended the big industrialists. It grouped among the polluters such giants as U. S. Steel and its subsidiary in Gary (the Gary Steel and Tin Mill), Youngstown Sheet and Tube Company, Inland Steel Company, Cities Service Petroleum Company, Sinclair Refining Company, Mobil Oil Company, and American Oil Company. Municipalities which have not treated their wastes came in for severe criticism too. Altogether 35 municipalities and 40 industrial establishments in Illinois and Indiana along the south end of the lake were said to cause "significant damage" to its waters.

Among the heaviest discharges, according to the report, is that of U. S. Steel at Gary. This plant poured into a channel (which flows into Lake Michigan) 230 million waste gallons a day, including 13,750 pounds of ammonia nitrogen, 1,500 pounds of phenol, 1,700 pounds of cyanide, and 54,000 pounds of oil. Comparable quantities of waste were unloaded, with devastating effects, by other industries along the shore. Most of the industries blandly answered that they were already treating their wastes. The heart of the government case was that the treatment was inadequate. At the conference the PHS, through Murray Stein, made several important recommendations: that water-quality standards be set for those areas near beaches and drinking-water intakes, that all industrial and municipal sewage receive secondary treatment before being discharged into the lake, and that industrial plants be required to take and keep samples of their wastes in an "open file."

Industry rebelled. The most publicized statement of the conference was made outside the conference room by a U. S. Steel official. Talking to reporters in the corridor, he ridiculed the government's recommendations as "pie-in-the-sky thinking." It was a damaging statement—for industry. When steel leaders learned of it, they called the local newspapers to try to have the statement deleted from later editions.

The government had based its recommendations on a strong case. The bitterest criticism of that case during the conference came from A. J. Cochrane of Youngstown Sheet and Tube (who appears in the discussion at the beginning of this book). "In some respects the data as presented are inaccurate," Cochrane told the conferrees, "but of greater significance, in our opinion, the report offers no real guidance for solution of the more difficult problems. The recommendation for exclusion of certain types of waste discharges is totally unreasonable for an area so heavily industrialized, and which uses such vast volumes of water in processing."

Clarence Klassen of the Illinois Sanitary Water Board challenged Cochrane's claim that the government's recommendations offered no solution. "It is a little contrary to my own conception of free enterprise on one hand for you to produce, and then look to someone else to solve your waste treatment problems . . . In other words, you solve the easy ones and when you get to the difficult ones you expect the government to give you the solution, is that correct?"

Not exactly, was the gist of Cochrane's lengthy reply. What he meant was that he would prefer to work out the solution with the state (which industry has used as its longtime patsy).

"I personally feel that you create the problem," Klassen said. "Therefore it is your responsibility to find the solution with whatever assistance you can get from the government, but basically the responsibility is yours."

Cochrane said industry would do its part but would also follow recommendations from the state.

Frank Chesrow, Chicago's Health Commissioner, put in a remark. "In other words," he said, "you will wait until it is pointed out to you before you do anything about it?"

Though Cochrane denied this, it was apparent that local officials were considerably upset by industry's attitude. Chesrow unmistakably expressed this dissatisfaction to the conferees. "In the past," he said, "most of our experience has been that industries didn't do anything about pollution until they were forced to. I recommend that the Attorney General start action in the United States District Court against these industries."

The government still hoped, in 1965, to work out the problem over a conference table instead of in a courtroom. The outlook remains clouded. Industry's remarks (in and out of the conference room) scarcely suggest the stirring of a collective conscience.

Seven: The Pollution Explosion

I

Friday morning, December 4, 1964, was clear and cold "Down East" on the Maine coast. A stiff wind blew, as it had most of the week, from the northeast. Oscar Carver, a lobster dealer on Beals Island, just across Mooseabec Reach from Jonesport on the mainland, left his office in a weathered frame building and walked down to the shore to look at his lobster pounds. What he saw first astonished and then nearly sickened him. Moving toward his pounds on the wind- and tide-driven water was a broad, ugly, yellowish-black mass. Quickly, his eyes scanned the opposite shore. There, at anchor off Jonesport's oil-storage depot, floated a large tanker. The oil, Oscar Carver realized, had escaped the tanker during the discharging operation. Helplessly, he watched the spreading mass blacken the offshore surf and then slowly begin to seep into his pounds. At that moment his lobster business was wiped out.

"It must have been five or six thousand gallons," Carver said later. "It got into my small pound first—the new one—and the lobsters just turned over and died. Then it got into the big pound. All week long after that the lobsters were crawling out of there up on the bank. I'd throw 'em back in the water, but they'd crawl right out again and die on the bank."

Oscar Carver and his wife were telling the story in the back of their country store, which was now the only business they had left. "We piled up the lobsters on the banks for the gulls to eat," Mrs. Carver said, "but the gulls wouldn't eat them. Why, the oil was so thick on their shells you couldn't *wash* it off them."

"Most pitiful sight I ever saw," a neighbor said. "It was close to high tide when the oil floated up on the shore. Then when the tide turned the lobsters were trying to climb up on the shore to breathe and that oil just washed back over them, and the lobsters were dying right there."

Carver called the Coast Guard. "By the time we got the call," a Coast Guard officer says, "the tanker had left. We sent investigators and they collected oil samples and took statements from available witnesses. This information was sent to the Corps of Engineers for further analysis and then to the Justice Department for final action."

Meanwhile, Carver was left with over 12,000 dead lobsters on his shore and an estimated loss of $20,000. The few surviving lobsters, their flesh badly tainted by oil, could not be sold for many months. He looked forward, eventually, to cleaning out his pounds, a long and dirty job. But for at least a year, Oscar Carver, who had been fishing for and dealing in lobsters for 25 years, would be out of the lobster business.

Despite his heartache and frustration, Oscar Carver may count himself more fortunate than most of us who are afflicted, in one way or another, by the noxious effects of polluted water. The wheels of justice, after a long delay, will grind out some redress for Carver's loss. Elsewhere, the circumstances may be less dramatic, the source of pollution less evident. How often have vacationers run expectantly down to a white sandy beach, only to find it caked at the shore line with practically indissoluble globs of oil! It was recently estimated that the world's shipping fleets discharge over one million tons of oil into the sea each year. We see only a small part of its ravages. In his section on phalaropes, the sandpiper-like little birds which feed buoyantly on the open water, Richard H. Pough writes in the *Audubon Water Bird Guide:* "To what extent the deadly fuel-oil droplets, that so mat a bird's feathers that they can no longer insulate the body from the cold sea water, have taken toll no one knows; but, like all sea birds, these must at times suffer from this modern scourge of oceanic bird life."

Yet much of the oil which escapes, deliberately or accidentally, from tankers eventually shows up along our shores. Both public beaches and private property are marred by its tar-like residue. In southern seas the warmer water tends to break down the oil and dissolve it, but the oil clings to northern coasts sometimes for years. It is especially disastrous to wildfowl, with individual kills running into the many-thousands during storms when ducks, seeking shelter, flock to bays covered by oil which has been jettisoned by foundering ships. Aside from the disgust of conservationists or gunners who see in such slaughter a special waste of our natural resources, there is the pity most of us feel at the sight of wild things tortured and killed by substances that man heedlessly turns loose in the environment. Even small amounts of oil can prove fatal to ducks and other water birds. Matting their feathers, it allows cold water and air to reach their skins, freezing them to death; ingested, it coats their insides with poisonous material; in other variations, it weighs the birds down so that they drown or are immobilized and starve to death.

While oil that is released at sea causes untold damage, its effects are more evident in smaller bodies of water. Thousands of ducks were killed, for instance, when the tanker *Pine Branch* went aground in the St. Lawrence River in 1948. An even more disastrous kill occurred in the upper Mississippi River during the winter of 1962-63. It was caused by two separate oil spills. One took place at the Richards Oil Company of Savage, Minnesota, where a pipeline carrying industrial oils cracked and allowed approximately one million gallons to escape into the Minnesota River. At nearly the same time several storage tanks belonging to the Honeymead Products Company of Mankato, Minnesota, ruptured and released three million gallons of crude soybean and salad oil. (Much of this oil was recovered by the company; though unfortunately a bulldozer scraping it from the ice on nearby Blue Earth River crashed through the ice into the water.) In the spring, torrents of industrial and soybean oils were released by the thaw and carried into the Mississippi River. Coinciding with the peak of migration, this deadly flow destroyed many thousands of ducks and raised fears for the safety of human beings. The Executive Council of Minnesota declared a state of emergency, while Governor Rolvaag called the National Guard to duty and asked assistance from the United States Public Health Service. A careful check of the polluted water was kept by the PHS, and there were no outbreaks of disease or illness among human beings. Because of the public's concern, however, the Minnesota Legislature passed the model "Rosenmeier Bill," prohibiting the storage of any liquid not properly retained against entry into state waters.

It is true that most of the oil pollution in American waters is the result of accidents. Tanks burst, ships run aground, and oil escapes. (Many apologists for the oil and shipping industries have successfully averted criticism from themselves by pointing to the enormous number of tankers sunk dispersing their oil during World War II; it is a good guess, however, that if all the oil pollution attributed to the depredations of Nazi submarines were valid, there would have been so little oil available Allied planes and tanks would never have been able to function.) Unfortunately, it is also true that much oil pollution results from the deliberate pumping out of ships' tanks and bilges by unconscionable captains. Here passenger and dry-cargo ships are as much at fault as oil tankers. All ships take on sea water for ballast. As a ship's fuel tanks empty, they are filled with salt water and so oily wastes are created. Approaching port, its ballast no longer needed, the ship pumps out its tanks, just as tankers clean and pump out their oil storage tanks. In either case, long-lived concentrations of oil are spread across the sea.

World opinion has reacted sharply to this practice. In 1954, an international convention proposed restrictions on the disposal of oily wastes in coastal waters. Seventeen nations signed the compact, but pressure from the oil and shipping industries prevented the treaty's ratification by the United States. By 1961 the situation had grown so critical that the United States altered its position, and in 1962 emerged as a leading force for reform at the international conference held in London. The evolution of law has infused further life into the prosecution of polluters. At one time a court was likely to rule that oil was not "refuse," and so its disposal in rivers or coastal waters was not a violation of law. This interpretation of oil pollution has come to be questioned by the United States Court of Appeals. When the federal government prosecuted the Ballard Oil Company of Hartford, Connecticut, for pumping 6,700 barrels of oil into the Connecticut River (the oil overflowed after being pumped into a tank already filled to capacity) the case went to the Court of Appeals. The court ruled that oil was indeed refuse since after its escape its industrial purpose terminated, and a definition of refuse does not require that a material be deliberately thrown away. Stiffer state supervision has also begun to restrict the polluters. California, for instance, requires that samples of oil be taken from outgoing tankers; later, if concentrations of oil are found along the coast, they may be associated with the samples held by the state.

A number of oil companies have fallen into step with public opinion. Some have conducted extensive research to find ways of cutting down their pollution. In 1964 the Standard Oil Company of New Jersey (ESSO) announced the discovery of a means by which oil and salt water may be separated into their component parts. If this is introduced widely into tanker fleets, ships will be able to retain oil residues in their tanks while discharging pure salt water back to the sea.

Ironically, while commercial shipping may have been converted to sound conservation practices, some longtime victims have stepped into the role of seagoing menace. Today mounting thousands of vacationers, long troubled by commercial oil pollution, are injecting our waterways with obnoxious dosages of outboard motor wastes. The relatively infinitesimal amounts of these wastes now in the water have been proven by laboratory tests to affect the taste and odor of fish taken from them and cooked: what effects these increasing wastes will have on human health has not been determined. Until now, most local efforts to regulate the use of boats on lakes set aside primarily for fishing and swimming have been defeated by the boating and equipment manufacturers.

II

In the summer of 1963 an inspection party of sportsmen and state legislators picked its way over the site of an abandoned strip mine in western Pennsylvania. Spoil banks of earth and broken rock towered above the barren landscape. Orange fluid moved sluggishly through a stream bed, supporting no life but lending its garish color to the bordering rocks and mud. The men stared at the bleakness around them. Only a few years before this land had been rich in game, and through it had run Little Scrubgrass Creek, one of the finest trout streams in Butler County. That was before the miners had come for the bituminous coal which lay in seams near the earth's surface.

There were questions from both the sportsmen and the legislators. A member of the state health department explained that the state felt obligated to grant permits to the miners to begin operations again elsewhere, because the miners claimed it would bankrupt them to backfill the land and prevent the discharge of acid into nearby streams as the law required. Since the state did not have the money to clean up behind them, it kept on granting the miners permits while hoping that eventually they would return to finish the job at the last place.

State Senator Robert Fleming of Aspinwall shook his head in disgust. "It's the same as playing a slot machine," he said. "You keep putting in more money in the hope of getting back what you've already poured down the slot. The only trouble is the jackpot comes up so seldom."

This scene—desolation calling up responses of anger and disgust—has become a commonplace in rural Pennsylvania and its neighboring states in recent years. Each year three and a half million tons of acid wastes seep from mines, active and abandoned, into the nation's streams. Almost all of this pollution occurs east of the Mississippi River in the great coal-mining areas of Pennsylvania, West Virginia, Kentucky, Ohio, and other states about "Appalachia." In most of these states, stream pollution officials insist that acid mine drainage is the "worst pollution problem." According to Pennsylvania's United States Senator Joseph S. Clark, it is "the toughest resource problem in America today. No single approach seems to solve it. It has sterilized thousands of miles of streams—2,000 in my state alone—strangled the economic life of hundreds of communities, killed billions of fish, and renders the prospects of many areas of the country dim indeed unless we are prepared to launch a massive assault upon it and bring it under control."

Scientists today do not quite understand the process by which the water seeping into the mines under natural conditions emerges again as a deadly fluid smothering the life in every stream it can reach. It has always been a vexing problem in the traditional "deep mines" of the Pennsylvania coal fields. It seems to be an even more destructive one in the strip mines which scar so many rural areas in the East. Despite all the bad publicity it has received in recent years, strip mining is not necessarily an evil. It is a mining technique which extracts, at comparatively low cost, veins of valuable coal near the earth's surface. The top soil is stripped off and there lies the coal, conveniently at hand. The earth does not have to be undermined by shafts, tunnels, and galleries. The miners can work in the open air.

If the strip miners fulfilled their responsibilities to the community, the problem would be considerably alleviated. But too many of them have extracted the coal and then cleared out, claiming it was unprofitable to repair the gouged earth. So great holes are left in the earth, and over them tower unsightly mountains of soil and debris. Rain and ground water collect in the depressions, mingling with acid-bearing material. It is the common belief that these materials, exposed to water and air, form the deadly pools of sulphuric acid (though this acid has also formed, inexplicably, in mines sealed off from the air). Heavy rains inevitably wash the acid into nearby streams, carrying it miles away to kill all the animal and vegetable life in its path. By a sinister turn of events, the pollution here is self-perpetuating. In most cases, when the polluting industry closes down, the supply of wastes to nearby streams is cut off; miners, creating cavities in the earth, bequeath to the area a receptacle which continues to collect and mix the deadly ingredients.

A recent report by the League of Women Voters indicates that the oldest known strip mine in Pennsylvania dates back to 1815, and is still discharging its damaging chemicals to nearby streams. Acid mine drainage, according to old records, was not unknown as a killer to our ancestors. A Pennsylvania report of 1860 described the effects of mine drainage in the Schuylkill River, where all of the fish were killed in an area above Reading. Yet another record reveals that a Pennsylvania judge refused to award damages in 1886 to people whose property had been damaged by mine drainage; it was said to be part of a stream's "natural flow."

In this century, mine drainage, like most other forms of pollution, has overwhelmed one stream after another. It cannot be said that the public is unaware of the problem. Streams blighted by sulphuric acid pose only a minor public health problem because they are so obnoxious to eye or nose that no one would be tempted to drink from them. Even where the waters are outwardly pure, a garish yellow or orange substance (called "Yellow Boy" by the miners) coats the rocks along streambeds. Concerned people, for the most part, long ago centered their attention on the strip miners. There are public-spirited men among the "strippers," of course, mine operators who backfill the land to contour after the coal has been extracted, planting new vegetation to prevent erosion and filling in depressions which might collect the destructive mixture of water and acid. Yet a high percentage of the strip miners are "gypsies." There is almost the smell of death and decay about these men, who invade a community to strip it not only of its coal but of its well-being, too. To the farmer or landowner they offer royalties on the coal extracted from his land, but leave him with poisoned streams and useless, debris-heaped acres. To the laborers they offer jobs (usually at non-union wages), and leave them after a short time with a devastated countryside and a water supply totally unfit for the use of any other industry which might have considered settling there. Jobs dry up. Tax revenues from the stripped land dwindle to almost nothing. Hunters and fishermen, who once had brought tourist dollars, no longer come.

A "Clean Streams" law passed by the Pennsylvania State Legislature in 1945 failed to stop the strip miners. It prohibited them from allowing mine drainage to reach "clean streams," but allowed them to do their worst to streams already polluted. Once polluted, always polluted, seemed to be the decision of Pennsylvania lawmakers. The law, such as it was, had no teeth and no means of enforcing it. The miners continued to pollute new streams and, when caught, absolved themsevles on the grounds that the water was "already polluted." Nobody disputed them. By the 1960's 3,000 of Pennsylvania's 45,000 miles of streams were classified as "acid." Typical of the damage inflicted was that by the one mining company which, in 1961, cut into a flooded mine near Ohiopyle. The acid water rushed into nearby Cucumber Run, prompting the Pittsburgh *Press* to print the following "obituary of a stream."

"Little Cucumber Run which once gleamed blue and

white as it tumbled over the 30-foot high ledge into a shady gorge is now a rust-colored stream that looks like the discharge water from an industrial plant . . . The water, which had a very offensive odor, swept downstream and at South Connellsville bathers were driven from the water by the stain and by the dead fish floating downstream."

Other examples of strip-mining ravages piled up. At Snowden an 11-year old boy fell from a 60-foot embankment left by strippers into a pool of stagnant water. The pool was 35 feet deep. The boy drowned before help arrived. In Butler and Clarion Counties highly acid water seeped into springs and wells at which farmers watered their cattle. Cattle sickened, and many calves were born dead. A stripper whose mine drainage had killed 1,200 trout in a stream near Blandburg was forced to pay the state $2,500 damages. A local sportsman's group counted 16 trout streams polluted by strippers in their area of western Pennsylvania.

The streams were so blatantly polluted that, shunned by everyone, they were not generally considered a public health menace. Most of the streams were short and did not flow beyond Pennsylvania's boundaries to create an instance of "interstate pollution." Outside help, therefore, could be expected as a result of neither issue. Unorganized, the state's conservationists and sportsmen were ineffective in their effort to strike back at the polluters. They wrote indignant letters to the newspapers and told each other that the strip-mine operators were scoundrels. John F. Laudadio, then the legislative chairman of the Pennsylvania Federation of Sportsmen's Clubs (and later a state representative), issued a report in 1959 that said, "Strip miners create rural slums, blighted areas, death traps, poisoned water, and depressed areas." But the fact that conservationists were morally right made little difference. The strip miners had powerful friends in the state legislature, and only there could the laws be changed to compel miners to leave the land and streams as they had found them. The conservationists imagined the conflict to be one of "rights." The miners knew it to be one of power.

One of the conservationists' bitterest foes in the state legislature was Democratic Senator John J. Haluska of Cambria County. Haluska, a politician who liked to wear diamond stickpins, had had a curious career. Though not a medical man, he championed the controversial Hoxsey Cancer Cure in Pennsylvania; but later agreed in federal court to dissolve his clinics. Though not a lawyer, he had tried to run for the bench in common pleas court, claiming he was as "learned in the law" as some judges he knew; the state Attorney General's office declared him ineligible.

Haluska represented a strong strip mining area in the Pennsylvania State Senate. As chairman of the Senate's Commission on Local Government, he was known as a politician of considerable influence. The conservationists accused him of holding back their "clean streams" bills. The controversy flared into the open in 1961 when the Pittsburgh *Press* revealed that Haluska was driving around Harrisburg in an automobile owned by a prominant strip miner. Haluska resorted to the traditional strategy of an affronted legislator. He charged the *Press* with trying "to influence or coerce legislation" and ordered its editor, W. W. Forester, to appear before his committee. Forester replied that he would not come, and the matter was dropped.

There were other attempts to silence all opposition to

unrestricted strip mining. Lobbyists for the industry distributed around the state copies of a brochure illustrated by photographs of a beautiful stream. This stream and the land around it, the brochure informed readers, were a part of the Pine Creek area that had been extensively strip-mined. The brochure was exposed as a fake by a relentless and highly vocal conservationist named William E. Guckert.

"That's not Pine Creek in the picture," said Guckert, who had toured the area. "The real Pine Creek area is a mess and the creek is free of acid only in the summer—when it's dry!"

A Pittsburgh taxidermist, Guckert has been the loudest and most effective conservationist (if not always the best liked, even among the sportsmen's ranks) in Pennsylvania. He bristles with the righteous indignation vital to the success of any crusading group. The source of his indignation is his personal experience. Before World War II Guckert bought a farm in Butler County. There were a dozen clear, well-stocked trout streams in the area. One of the best was Little Scrubgrass Creek, where Guckert often fished during the hours he was away from his business. Then, in 1948, strip miners began to extract coal near the head of the creek. Guckert's thick neck reddens and his eyes bulge with rage when he talks about strip miners.

"One stripper came in and ruined 12 miles of stream," Guckert says. "Later on they claimed the streams had already been polluted by deep mines in the area. Well, the trout didn't seem to know about it. They were thriving until the strippers came along."

To fight the strip miners Guckert learned all he could about mining techniques. His most crippling handicap in the struggle was the absence of a united front among the conservationists and sportsmen. But Guckert was persistent and his voice ("He's the guy who talks like a machine gun," one of the strippers has said of him) was beginning to be heard. In 1959 a mild bill was proposed in the state legislature which would require strippers to backfill (or round off) abandoned mines to 50 percent of the high wall of debris. Senator Frank Koprever, chairman of the Mines and Minerals Committee, did not report the bill out of his committee.

Guckert was furious. He asked the conservationists to ignore party lines, and began to wield the 12,000-member Allegheny County Sportsmen's League (of which he was executive secretary) as a political hammer. He asked the Democratic Party in Duquesne to submit a candidate to run against Republican Frank Koprever on a conservation platform. The Democrats responded by nominating an unlikely candidate—a Duquesne lawyer named Leonard C. Staisey. Because of a childhood accident, Staisey is practically blind. He had been defeated four years earlier by Koprever (who was also mayor of Duquesne) by 14,000 votes. Now, in 1960, Guckert led sportsmen and conservationists in getting out the vote for Staisey. They put up 26 large billboards supporting his candidacy, distributed 50,000 cards and mailed 16,000 letters. Staisey, the conservationist, defeated Koprever this time by 32,000 votes.

Organized, the clean-streams advocates were getting results. In the next election Guckert went after four prominent opponents of anti-strip-mine legislation and all four were defeated at the polls. The movement began to spread through the state. M. Graham Netting, a veteran conservationist who is the director of Pittsburgh's Carnegie Museum, became a staunch ally of the rough-and-ready Bill Guckert. Netting broadened the attack. "All of us, regardless of deeds in bank vaults, are but sojourners on the earth's surface," Netting wrote. "No one, during his brief occupancy, has the moral right to ruin land, pollute a stream, or destroy a forest, and leave the area less habitable than when his stewardship began."

A vital step forward in Pennsylvania's conservation struggle took place in 1962 with the formation of "The Clean Streams Minutemen." A group of the state's most prominent conservationists and sportsmen, headed by Ross Leffler, a former Assistant Secretary of the Interior under President Eisenhower, Dr. Netting of the Carnegie Museum, and Carl White, president of the Federation of Pennsylvania Sportsmen's Clubs, founded the organization. Here was a united front at last—a non-profit organization formed to push clean-streams legislation at Harrisburg. The League of Women Voters, the Garden Clubs, the Roadside Council, and other interested groups cooperated in its program.

The Minutemen were organized at a critical point in the 1962 gubernatorial campaign. William Scranton was opposed by Richardson Dilworth, who had the backing of Pennsylvania's powerful Democratic organization, led by David Lawrence. Democratic registration in the state exceeded Republican registration by 160,000. Guckert's Allegheny County Sportsmen asked the two candidates for a statement on clean-streams legislation which had been opposed by the strip-mining interests. Scranton came out for a strong bill; Dilworth said that he could not give the sportsmen an answer until he had talked over the matter with Lawrence.

Guckert maintained an unusual silence until the day

that President Kennedy arrived in Pittsburgh to endorse Dilworth's candidacy. Then, with perfect timing, he announced that his sportsmen's organization would back Scranton in the election. Thousands of votes were involved. The news made headlines in the Pittsburgh papers, blunting the impact of Kennedy's visit.

"We knew you were going to back Scranton," a Democratic friend said afterwards to Guckert. "But you couldn't have picked a worse time to announce it. You killed us."

Pennsylvania's other conservation groups, many of which generally prefer to remain politically neutral, followed by endorsing Scranton in the clean-streams program. Sportsmen's groups sent to each of its members a copy of a letter written by Scranton ("Dear Fellow Sportsmen," it began). "The first and most essential thing we need in the conservation field is a strip mining bill with real teeth," Scranton wrote. "Forests, streams, lakes and wildlife are not temporary boosts. They are permanent resources, which may assure the health and prosperity of generations yet unborn."

The clean-streams program became one of the campaign's most vital issues. United, Pennsylvania's conservationists and sportsmen (there are one million hunting licenses and 500,000 fishing licenses sold in the state each year) provided a formidable segment of voters. Scranton captured a normally Democratic Allegheny County (Pittsburgh) and, though two of his running mates on the Republican state-wide ticket lost, went on to defeat Dilworth by 471,591 votes.

The result seemed to have an immediate effect on the legislators at Harrisburg. Scranton proposed, and the legislature enacted, a strong clean-streams bill during the 1963 session. It required miners of bituminous coal to be licensed and to post bonds before beginning a stripping operation, to backfill the land in accordance with prescribed standards, and to prevent acid drainage from seeping into adjacent streams. Stiff penalties were established for violators of this law. It is considered by many stream-control experts to be a model law (Kentucky later enacted a similar one) and may prove a significant step in the struggle against America's "worst pollution problem."

A law, however, is a mockery without strong enforcement. One guarantee that Pennsylvania's clean-streams law would not be such a mockery was the composition of the five-member Land Reclamation Board established by its provisions. In addition to three state officers, the board includes one representative of conservation interests and one of strip-mining interests. The conservation interests selected Bill Guckert.

"We're putting teeth in this cockeyed law," Guckert said after joining the board. There was a tone in his insistent voice which seldom appears in that of disinterested political appointees. Here, in action by the concerned citizen, America may find the best way to shackle those who have poisoned its waterways.

III

"In the spring of this year two-year-old Gerald Colpas toddled into the kitchen of his new Lindenhurst, Long Island, home and asked for a drink of water. His mother drew it from a two-gallon camping jug that had been filled in another community. Beside the jug a covered fish tank held the reserve supply. Gerald's thirst quenched, Mrs. Colpas started filling a cooking pot from the tap in the sink. Thick suds foamed up over the edge before it was half full. The clean, crisp-looking suds were caused by synthetic detergents that had contaminated the ground water table after having seeped from cesspools and septic tanks in the neighborhood."

The paragraph quoted above is not the lead to a scare story dreamed up by a sensation-hunting local reporter. It is the introduction to a detailed scientific paper prepared in 1962 by Edward Wise, a specialist in science and technology attached to Washington's Library of Congress. It is simply another description of the curious modern pollution which has affected what one detergent industry spokesman has blandly dismissed as "less than ten percent" of our population. But it has alarmed a much greater proportion of our population to such an extent that a powerful industry has reluctantly conformed to public opinion. Though grave problems remain, an optimist might see these developments as a milestone in the American people's struggle to reclaim part of their plundered natural resources.

The incident described in Mr. Wise's report is not unique. Of 600 wells analyzed in Long Island's Suffolk County recently, 35 percent were found to be contaminated by detergent wastes. Of 54,000 private wells analyzed around Minneapolis and St. Paul in Minnesota, half were similarly contaminated. A sea of suds pouring from the faucets of Montgomery County, Maryland, homeowners just outside Washington triggered outraged protests to legislators and administrators in the nation's capitol. In a single incident near Kearny, Nebraska, detergent wastes seeping into the ground traveled 4,000 feet in 14 months to infiltrate a private well. Although detergent pollution has manifested itself in many more spectacular ways, it is through the pollution of ground water that it has raised the greatest anxiety and will surely prove the most insidious and persistent threat to the public's well-being.

"Detergent chemicals," according to Wisconsin's Senator Gaylord Nelson, "which do not decompose are polluting our underground wells, and the rivers, lakes, and streams which are used as a public water supply. Through constant reuse of this water, the detergent pollution is building up steadily."

While detergents pose nagging problems even in remote areas, the impact of their foaming wastes is most damaging in the vast suburban complexes which appeared after World War II. Here, in the interests of economy, sewers tying into the big municipal systems often have not been laid. Wastes, instead of being carried away, are channeled into septic tanks and cesspools, devices adequate for organic sewage but incapable of grappling with certain chemicals used in synthetic detergents. Effect follows cause as night the day. Take a dense concentration of cleanly, doubly-gadgeted, triply-children'd middle-class families and their accumulated dirty laundry and dishes, pour in an appropriate share of the one and a half million tons of synthetic detergents bought annually by American housewives, and the result is a mountain of the creamy, long-lasting suds promised by television hucksters. The suds (or, more accurately, a special component of the detergents) are long-lasting, make no mistake about it. Flushed down the drain, they soon reappear, visually if not chemically identical, in somebody else's glass of water.

"Detergent" is the word used technically to describe all soaps and cleaning agents (even sand, when used in scrubbing), but recently it has been popularly restricted to the synthetic detergents used in the home. Soaps, previously our chief detergents, are made of animal and vegetable fats. Synthetic detergents, with petroleum derivatives as their base, were developed in Germany during World War I when that country turned to "ersatz" products after the Allied blockade had cut off its supply of animal fats. Such detergents, not introduced here on a large scale until after World War II, proved to be immensely effective. Old-fashioned soaps are poor cleansers in "hard" water, but the new detergents retain their effectiveness in all types of water. Their chief cleaning agent is alkyl benzene sulfonate. Under its abbreviated name, ABS, this component has gained notoriety because it is the substance which does not break down under ordinary sewage treatment.

Suds, of course, were on the scene long before synthetic detergents. The soap flakes (such as Rinso) which appeared on the market after World War I based their appeal to buyers on the point that now the rubbing-and-scrubbing bar soaps of grandma's day had been replaced by miracle flakes in which the housewife got her clothes clean primarily by soaking and rinsing. Suds, which actually do not serve any purpose in the cleaning process, were slowly introduced as a psychological attraction. Women leaped at the bait; perhaps the modern chemical and gadget-ridden world is so puzzling to most of us, offering so little to our senses, that the spectacle of snowy suds bubbling up from a tub of dirty laundry satisfies some dim craving for the sensual world of the past. In any case, suds became a commodity. The three giant manufacturers of soap products, Procter and Gamble, Lever Brothers, and Colgate-Palmolive, continued to add suds-producing components to certain of their laundry flakes, components whose utility approximates that of the magician's *abracadabra,* but whose allure to the gullible is just as strong. The "Floods of Suds" advertised on the boxes of pre-war Supersuds foamed up into the "Oceans of Suds" promised by the post-war makers of Tide. It was an example of chemistry reverting to the humbug of alchemy.

But the chemistry which transforms the sparkling fluff of domestic suds to the pesty billows which emerge in the wild is quite valid. In being washed down the drain, the household suds lose their identity. They break up, but that component known as ABS persists. Where the animal or vegetable bases of ordinary soaps were consumed by the bacteria in septic tanks and cesspools, the petroleum-derived ABS reacts with the bacteria to cause foam. No more than half of the ABS entering a septic tank is broken down, and the rest may seep out, find its way to the general flow of ground water, and eventually be carried along into wells and other sources of the local water supply. Since the ABS does not break down for many weeks, it inevitably reappears in the cloudy, or perhaps foamy, water glass of some dismayed housewife nearby.

The same housewife often plays an unwitting part in the process, using a disproportionate load of detergents both at home and in the many coin-operated laundries which have sprung up in suburban areas. In this the housewife is abetted by the detergent manufacturers, whose product comes in boxes with suspiciously roomy openings marked off by the dotted line. Everybody has experienced the tipping up of a box of chips and suddenly losing control of the situation. The chips come tumbling out until there is a heaping sinkful—another potential flood of suds. An accident? Not from the manufacturer's point of view.

The detergent industry, as sensitive as any other when its contributions to mankind are minimized by a finicky public, has tried to obscure the floods of suds under an ocean of words. Like the detailed work of Biblical scholarship described by Samuel Butler in *The Way of All Flesh,* the detergent industry has published favorable reports on its product so exhaustive that they exhaust anyone who has ever had anything to do with them. The reports contend that detergents add neither taste nor odor to the water they pollute. This, apparently, is true. Studies made by the Public Health Service confirm the absence of taste and odor despite the avowal by many people that detergents taste and smell awful. According to a PHS report, "ABS alone at the concentration usually found in finished water cannot be the cause of either taste or odor. ABS is always accompanied by other contaminants from domestic or industrial sources, however, and the reported taste and odor must be attributed to these contaminants."

The industry is on less firm ground when it contends that detergent wastes in public water supplies are not a hazard to health. The Public Health Service has set a recommended standard of not more than 0.5 milligram per liter in drinking water. When asked if scientists can say that detergent wastes are not harmful to human health, Richard L. Woodward of the PHS has answered: "I think that is an impossible statement for anyone to make about anything. I would say that the evidence to date does not lead us to believe that our limit in the drinking water standards was not a reasonable one."

A number of studies have been made here and abroad to see if detergents induce cancer in rats and mice. Because all of the studies so far have been short-term ones, scientists do not feel they are conclusive. But studies made on the eggs and larvae of clams and oysters have shown that detergents are definitely harmful to them; eggs failed to develop, and larvae perish, in water containing common amounts of detergent wastes. Detergents, like oil, also destroy the "waterproofing" qualities of a wildfowl's feathers.

A queer defense of detergents appears in industry's persistent claim that its wastes are really a boon to the public health. This industry argument, which Wisconsin's Congressman Henry S. Reuss has called "the sudsy detective apology," is to the effect that the presence of foam in drinking water serves as a warning that other, more harmful, contaminants may also be present. If detergents are seeping from septic tanks and entering the public water supply, then the non-lethal doses of detergents are telling the public that there is something wrong with the septic tanks. Congressman Reuss has demolished this gush of silliness.

"Outside of the somewhat illogical aspect of this thing," he said, "it is as if a proprietor of a 'greasy spoon' restaurant were to say, 'Isn't it a wonderful thing you see lipstick on your coffee cup, because that shows our dishwashing procedures aren't very sanitary.'

"Occasionally a septic tank that is on the bum and is not working may spread typhoid germs around the country. If the unhappy neighbor notices that his water is foaming and takes it over to be analyzed at the chemists, and if the chemical analysis shows that the water contains (a) detergents and (b) typhoid germs, then he may well say, 'God bless Procter and Gamble.' But he will be one in a million."

The solution, according to many conservationists and legislators, has always been comparatively simple. For some time there has been a movement underway among these people to force the detergent industry into converting to bio-degradable products—those which will break down under ordinary sewage treatment. The industry has desultorily researched this project for some years, much too slowly to suit its critics. For the development of "good" detergents, the industry has spent about $5 million a year, which is something less than 99 and 44/100 percent of the $250 million it has spent each year on advertising its "bad" detergents. By 1965 the industry, goaded to a greater effort by the threat of national legislation that would make the conversion mandatory, placed its biodegradable detergents on the market. The offending ABS has been replaced by a new component called linear alkylate sulfonate. Lesser known brands containing the new component had been marketed earlier and bought by housewives worried by the effects of the "bad" detergents. In Ridgefield, Connecticut, and other towns the members of the local garden clubs peddled boxes of the new detergents and donated their proceeds from sales to various conservation projects.

The big detergent companies themselves introduced the new product without much fanfare. As one of their officials said, "'We Have Stopped Polluting the Water!' is not a constructive advertising slogan." Temporarily, at least, the detergent industry, supported by the giant chemical corporations (Union Carbide, Continental Oil, Monsanto, etc.) which manufacture the chemical components, had staved off the threat of federal legislation. When Senator Muskie's anti-pollution bill was passed by the Senate in 1965 there was no mention in it of standards for detergents. Yet many experts remain skeptical of the "new" component.

"For years the detergent industry has been getting by on the promise that a new degradable product was in the works," a Public Health Service officer has said. "Now the new detergent is here, and while it seems to break down all right in the big modern municipal treatment plants, it's the same old story in the septic tanks. The wastes simply do not break down. So—where do we go from here?"

Eight: The City and State in Crisis

I

In 1965 New York City, built at the mouth of one of the great rivers of the western hemisphere, braced itself to combat a crippling water shortage; the city manager of Troy, New York, defending his city against charges that it had converted its stretch of that river into the most polluted body of water in the state, replied that schools, urban renewal, and highways were "far more important to Troy than sewage treatment"; and Governor Nelson Rockefeller, in a drastic reversal of his "pay-as-you-go" financial policy, proposed a $1.7 billion program to clean up New York's waterways. A water shortage, an uncooperative public, a staggering bill: these three stories symbolize the tangle of frustrations which an industrial state, once mired in pollution, finds barring its return to respectability.

New York City has struggled with water problems since colonial days. Huddled then at the foot of Manhattan Island, the city turned its back on the Hudson River because at that point it had already mingled with the salty tidal water rushing up the bay. Later, when engineers conceived their plans for bringing fresh water from afar, long segments of the Hudson (Henry Hudson's "Great River of the Mountains") were already polluted. The lakes of upstate Croton were tapped and their water brought to the city by aqueducts. Additional upstate lakes were converted to reservoirs for the city as its population grew. In desperation, New York turned to the Delaware River in the 1920's but New Jersey and Pennsylvania, through which the Delaware flows after it leaves New York State, fought to keep the river's water for themselves. The United States Supreme Court ruled in 1931 that New York City might take 400 million gallons a day for itself. Still the city's demands for water were unsatisfied.

Finally, to prevent federal intervention in their affairs, the states of the Delaware River Basin formed an interstate compact known as "Incodel," and agreed to build a system of dams and reservoirs to control the river's flow. The heavy flows of spring are contained by the dams and reservoirs, rather than allowed to escape to the sea, and are rationed out during the course of the year. New York City was thus guaranteed 800 million gallons a day, and the rights of the "Incodel" states ostensibly protected. (In reality, the Delaware becomes "horribly polluted" after it leaves New York State, so that Philadelphia, Camden, and other cities tapping its flow are confronted by a massive purification project.)

The heavy drought which sapped water supplies in the Northeast during the early 1960's at last affected even New York City's enormous reserve (the city normally uses more than 1.2 billion gallons a day.) In 1965 the city's reservoirs shrank to less than half of capacity and officials organized a "save water" campaign. Once more there were suggestions that the city tap the Hudson's vast flow. A dozen years before this crisis, a management survey had suggested New York City could solve its water problems by installing meters in every building (building owners there now pay a flat water rate every year), repairing leaks, and utilizing the Hudson. "Hudson River water," the report said, "with filtration and chemical treatment properly handled under standard methods, can be made equal to the water now delivered to New York City in safety, color, taste and other elements of quality." This line of reasoning was based on the belief that the Hudson's water, many miles north of the city, was comparatively free of pollution; it could be brought to the city by aqueduct over long distances, just as water comes from upstate reservoirs.

Although none of the experts quarrelled with recommendations to meter the water and repair the leaks, there was considerable doubt about the wisdom of drinking Hudson River water. Towns and industries bordering the river long ago had destroyed its purity. Shad fishing, at one time, was a flourishing spring industry along the Hudson near New York City. The quality of Hudson shad, however, has declined with the quality of its water. Most of the fishermen have given up. On a recent inspection of the Hudson shore near Stony Point, Senator Robert F. Kennedy approached a fisherman carrying a shad. "Is it good to eat?" he was quoted by the *New York Times* as asking the man.

"It's for baiting eel pots," the man told Kennedy. "Eating shad used to be good here, but not any more. You can taste the oil."

"Pollution?"

"I guess so," the man said.

After walking across a littered beach and examining the tan, opaque liquid dipped from the river in a glass, Kennedy turned to the people with him and said, "It's such a wasted asset. This could be a place where people swim and play. We have such tremendous natural resources. It's a crime against the present generation and against our children and our children's children to waste it like this."

No city along the Hudson can be proud of the contributions it has made to it in recent years, but Troy, a city of about 70,000 people just north of Albany, must rank among the worst. Troy is a textile town, now fallen on lean days. It has no sewage-treatment plant, has no money to build one, and, moreover, apparently sees no reason why it should. Admitting recently that Troy pollutes the Hudson, its city manager said, "and so does every other city."

Dr. Hollis S. Ingraham, New York State's Commissioner of Health, testifying before a congressional committee, gave an equally depressing, if not quite as fatalistic, picture of Troy's problem. "They are spread out along nine miles of the Hudson River," Ingraham said. "Every stream runs down to the Hudson, and every street does. And in every street there is a sewer running down. Now in order just to collect the sewage from this city it would be necessary to blast through solid rock for approximately nine miles along the waterfront and put in an intercepting sewer before you can even start to treat it."

The cost of laying the intercepting sewers (which would run perpendicular to the trunk sewers), collecting the sewage and carrying it to a treatment plant is estimated at $8 million; the cost of a treatment plant would be about $2 million. Pleading poverty, Troy is content to pour its raw sewage into the Hudson. The results of this policy were described at a recent health department hearing during which the state ordered the city to take action. There is little life in the Hudson near Troy except for a vicious species of eel which thrives on sewage. A sanitary engineer, attempting to take samples of the water near a Troy sewage outlet, was attacked by the eels. Others testified to the foul condition of the river there. According to the *New York Times*, "The testimony drove men to grit their teeth and three women to walk out of the hearing."

This, in varying degrees, is the story of long stretches of the river from Troy to New York. It is no wonder that New York City officials, proud of the quality of its drinking water, for a long time resisted every temptation to solve its problems by admitting the Hudson to its supply system. The city's position was best stated in a letter to the *New York Times*, dated May 10, 1965, by its Commissioner of Water Supply, Gas and Electricity, Armand D'Angelo.

"With reference to the use of the Hudson River as a source of water supply for New York City," D'Angelo wrote, "this matter was explored fully some fifteen years ago and the river was rejected as a highly polluted and undesirable source. In fact, in the decision of the Water

Power and Control Commission of the State of New York (1950), the Commission stated in part '. . . unless grave water supply crises arise such as to permit the acceptance of a water of inferior quality, the Commission does not believe the use of the river at or near the suggested point of diversion should be permitted as a source of permanent public water supply.'

"Since that time the quality of the Hudson River water has further deteriorated, with untreated sewage from human and industrial wastes being discharged directly into the river. This is a regrettable situation. If water from the Hudson River were now taken and made to commingle with our upland sources, it would but serve to degrade our high quality water of which we are so justly proud.

"Until the Hudson River is rendered free of pollution it is impossible for us to consider it as a source of water supply."

Yet, six weeks later, with the Northeast drought mounting in severity, D'Angelo was compelled to swallow these fine words. He asked New York City's Mayor Robert F. Wagner to reactivate a pumping station on the Hudson River just south of Poughkeepsie. This station had been built during the local drought of 1949-50 at a cost of $3 million. Tests, however, indicated that so much chlorine would have to be added to the river water to render it fit for human consumption that the station had been abandoned. By 1965, chlorine or not, the water looked better to official eyes. "The situation now demands that we investigate and develop emergency sources of supply to carry us over the current drought," D'Angelo told the mayor.

Plans were made to expand this pumping station to a capacity of 200 million gallons a day, putting it into operation early in 1966. Meanwhile, in April, 1965, the city had already turned to the use of river water in flushing its streets (the water having been treated chemically as a safeguard against contamination).

The most furious controversy along the Hudson in recent years has swirled around the projected construction of a power plant at Storm King Mountain. The Consolidated Edison Company, which supplies New York City with electricity, contends that it needs the plant to meet the city's growth. Conservationists believe that the plant could be placed elsewhere. Although the primary issue has been that the plant will destroy the scenic beauty of this area of the Hudson, there is also concern that the quality of the water will be altered in passing through the plant and so destroy many of the fish which are hatched nearby. Adding fuel to the controversy was Congressman Richard L. Ottinger, one of the most outspoken opponents of the new plant, who testified before the House Fisheries and Wildlife Subcommittee. In his testimony Ottinger charged that an atomic power plant, already built by Consolidated Edison on the Hudson south of Peekskill, had been responsible for the death of hundreds of thousands of fish. There had, Ottinger said, been an "effort by the state to hush up" the extent of the fish kill. He asked why, "some two years after the kill is reported to have started, there has been no prosecution of the company under existing state laws?"

One of Consolidated Edison's lawyers admitted that the kill was bad, "there's no question about it." But Harold G. Wilm, the State Commissioner of Conservation, who is felt by some conservationists to be a bit too lenient with industrial polluters, denied that his department had cooperated with Con Edison to cover up evidence of the fish kills. Absolving Con Edison, he called the kills "almost in the vein of an act of God." One can't help wondering whether, the big power companies having blamed their past depredations on almost everyone else, the next logical step isn't to shift the accusing finger toward a higher sphere.

While New York City, lying at the mouth of the Hudson, has been the recipient of a lot of other people's sewage, it contributes more than its share to the waters around it. Under the city's streets, wedged in with the telephone and electric wires, the gas mains and the subways, run 5,000 miles of sewers and 5,500 miles of water mains. In recent years it has struggled mightily to dilute the 500 million gallons of inadequately treated sewage it pumps into the surrounding waters every day. One recent sewage program cost the city $87 million; it is estimated that $450 million will be needed to complete the construction of interceptor sewers and treatment plants before the city's wastes will approach modern sanitary standards. Obviously, the richest city in the world, like poverty-ridden Troy, has been hampered in its quest of clear surrounding waters chiefly by a lack of money.

Occasionally sections of New York City have emitted a disproportionate share of untreated sewage because of more censurable shortcomings. Sewers, as well as bank vaults, lead men to dark deeds. The Borough of Queens was beset by a gaudy scandal in the 1920's when an investigation turned up a scarcity of sewers, and exorbitant payments for the few that were in use. The case remained in the headlines for some years, and properly so: One pipe salesman pocketed over $1,000,000 and lived in oriental splendor on Long Island, incriminating records were stolen, an important witness was murdered, and Borough President Maurice E. Connolly was sent to prison. Again in 1952 Queens was beset first by obnoxious odors, and then by a series of revelations which led two contractors and three city inspectors to the criminal courts. A brand-new sewer, costing the taxpayers almost $200,000, was found to have been caulked with rags and old newspapers to hide the leaks which had almost immediately appeared. The culprits received prison terms of up to eight and a half years.

A crisis of a less sinister, but equally obnoxious, nature occurred again in the borough during the summer of 1963. The residents of South Ozone Park and Howard Beach, Queens, complained of nasty odors originating around the Bergen Basin, a small arm of Jamaica Bay adjacent to the John F. Kennedy International Airport. Little attention was paid to the fuss at first because, for one thing, the waters of that area were so polluted that swimming was prohibited and, for another, there were no reported cases of serious illness. In late July, however, a local congressman appealed to President Kennedy for disaster aid to residents from whose houses the paint had begun to peel. At this point health authorities took a closer look at the situation. The subsequent report disclosed a series of miscalculations and misfortunes which were anything but entertaining to the harassed local residents.

To the northeast of Bergen Basin lies the Jamaica Bay Sewage Treatment Plant. This plant receives the raw sewage of nearly 500,000 people, or about 60 million gallons a day. Emptying into the basin nearby is a diversion line which ordinarily discharges only stormwater overflow. From October, 1962, until June, 1963, however, this diversion line discharged to Bergen Basin the entire volume of sewage consigned to the plant. The treatment plant itself, because it was being enlarged, had been closed down. No one, of course, expected the plant to be closed for eight months.

City Councilman Robert A. Low, in response to the inquiry of an interested citizen, wrote, "The rapid expansion in the population of Queens had apparently not been anticipated adequately by the Bureau of Water Pollution Control of the Public Works Department."

There were, in fact, all sorts of inquiries. Murray Stein, at the request of New York's Congressman John V. Lindsay, secured the following report from the Public Health Service's regional office: "The Jamaica Bay Sewage Treatment Plant was designed to provide primary treatment and chlorination at a capacity of 65 million gallons a day. Because of an increase in the population of the area, the plant was expanded to provide secondary treatment at a capacity of 100 million gallons a day (the entire project cost $15.5 million). The plant effluent is carried under the western portion of Idlewild Airport (later Kennedy Airport) and discharged into Jamaica Bay, not into Bergen Basin.

"The plan for the expansion of the plant provided for primary treatment and chlorination of all sewage prior to discharge into Jamaica Bay while the new facilities were being completed. During the construction operations, however, it was found that a trunk sewer leading into the plant, built in the early 1920's, was near collapse and in need of immediate replacement. A decision was made to bypass untreated wastes to Bergen Basin for several months during the replacement of the line. Because of a concrete truck drivers' strike and severe cold weather the replacement was not completed until mid-June, 1963.

"Because of the scarcity of rainfall this past spring and summer the sewage sludge, which accumulated in Bergen Basin during the replacement of the trunk sewer, has not been flushed out of the basin. The result has been the anaerobic decomposition of the sludge in the basin yielding hydrogen sulfide gas, the cause of the complaint made by the residents of the area."

The city finally took some action in the matter. Liquid sodium hypochlorite and solid sodium nitrate were applied to the basin and these chemicals alleviated the obnoxious odors. To disperse the accumulated sludge the city sent two fire boats to the basin. They pumped 100 gallons a minute into the sludge and stagnant water, hoping to stimulate a kind of tidal action, but the sludge proved immovable and the fire boats retired in defeat. At this point the New York City Board of Estimate appropriated $250,000 on an emergency basis to have the basin dredged. For a while there was a clamor to investigate the whole sorry mess to see if criminal negligence were involved but this flurry, like the odors, finally subsided. The quality of the Bergen Basin's waters returned to their normal state—unobtrusively polluted.

II

It is the attitude of New York State, like many other states, toward the "quality" of its water that causes much of the present confusion—and apparently some of the pollution. New York classifies each body of water in the state according to its "best usage in the public interest." Seven classes have been established, running from "AA" to "F"; Class "AA" and "A" waters are those fit for use as drinking supplies, while Class "F" may absorb almost any materials which do not render it a "public nuisance." To determine into which class a certain stream or lake fits, the state considers the use of its bordering lands, foreseeable water changes, and, significantly, the "extent of existing defilement." It is against the law to pour in materials which will alter a stream's classification.

It is obvious, then, that the classification of state waters, intended primarily to restrict pollution, is in reality simply a description of the waters. If a stream runs through a heavily-industrialized area and is already unfit for drinking, swimming, fishing, and any of the other uses the public would prefer to make of it, the stream is simply labelled Class "F" and written off. As Charles Callison of the National Audubon Society says, "Classification gives pollution a public sanction."

Just as state laws often "freeze" existing water quality standards indefinitely, they also grant a certain sanction to the polluters themselves. Countless industries do their worst to the surrounding waters under the protection of the notorious "Grandfather Clause." According to this agreement, a new industry is required to provide proper treatment for its effluent before discharging it into the state's waterways; but an industry already in business before the belated water pollution laws went into effect has a sort of license to pollute. New York, like other states, is reluctant to take action. "We have a large number of relatively small paper mills," Governor Rockefeller says in discussing polluting industries. "They are big offenders but important employers in upstate areas. We also have various chemical plants . . . We could say to an industry that they have got to stop. We could lose the industry. They would move from the state."

Because of the fear that the state would lose important industries, and because of the obvious inability of many towns and cities to raise the millions of dollars necessary to build interceptor sewers and treatment plants, Rockefeller decided upon a drastic new scheme. "If they were forced legally, it would cause chaos," he says. "Therefore, we have reluctantly come to this program after six years of attempt, in order to meet a reality which I think most of the citizens of our state want to meet."

Rockefeller's anti-pollution program for New York is the most ambitious yet undertaken by a state. It was undertaken partly because Rockefeller believes the states are capable of helping themselves. "There is a price to pay for having viable states," one of his aides says. "There must be *something* for them to do." But it was also undertaken because Rockefeller believes, as do most pollution experts, that the federal government's program of grants to municipalities for the construction of sewage-treatment facilities (authorized by the Federal Water Pollution Control Act) is sadly inadequate. He has pointed out that in recent years New York City alone has paid more for treatment construction than the total of Public Health Service grants to the entire United States. Though pollution is essentially an urban problem, this system of grants "discriminates" against cities: the federal government will pay 30 percent of the cost of municipal treatment plants—up to $600,000. (The Water Quality Act proposed to Congress in 1965 raises this limit to $1.2 million.) Since the costs of sewage treatment for large cities runs into the many millions of dollars, the government's contribution to them is negligible.

Rockefeller, himself, apparently had no idea of the extent of New York State's pollution problem until several years after he became governor in 1959. New York receives pollution from no other state and, except for the Raritan Bay area, exports very little to others. The official reports of state agencies concerned with water problems traditionally painted a bright picture of New York's lakes and streams (dedicated municipal authorities and selfless industrialists pushing ahead together toward their common vision of pure water). It came as something of a shock to the governor when a committee he had appointed to look into the state's major problems returned with a dismal description of its waterways. Nearly two-thirds of all New Yorkers—perhaps ten or 12 million people—live in areas blighted by pollution. Nearly 1,200 communities and 760 industrial sources feed raw or poorly treated wastes into state streams. It was estimated that $1,709,000,000 (twice the figure originally reported by the state) would be needed to meet the backlog of accumulated needs and the future needs for sewers and treatment plants through 1970.

It is to Rockefeller's credit that he drafted and put before the people his extensive plan. Halfway measures, he knew, would not succeed, for then the backlog of needs would never be dissipated. The governor's proposal was for the state to assume 30 percent of the costs of municipal treatment construction. Hopefully, the federal government would assume its 30 percent of the cost, and the state would petition Congress to raise the limit of government obligation so that it might pay its "rightful" share regardless of the size of a city's construction costs. However, until the government acted, the state was prepared to pay both its own share and that of the federal government—a total of 60 percent of the needed $1.7 billion. To pay its projected part of the cost, Rockefeller proposed a billion-dollar state bond issue. To encourage local communities to raise the other 40 percent of the costs, the state had already lifted until 1973 the constitutional debt limits of those communities borrowing for sewage construction. To encourage industries to provide treatment for their wastes, Rockefeller proposed a series of tax incentives, allowing industries a one-year write-off for construction and removing the approved expenditures from local real property taxes.

In putting his plan before the people in 1965, Rockefeller was able to point to a number of "horrible examples." One was Gloversville, a Mohawk Valley town suffering from the recent prolonged drought. Though there was an ample flow of water in Cayadutta Creek, which runs through the town, Gloversville's untreated domestic sewage and the grease and bits of animal flesh from its 12 tanneries made the water, as a large, red-lettered sign nearby warned, "unfit for human consumption." Rockefeller reported that the creek is "so polluted with sewage and grease that it would foul the pumps of fire engines."

Equally polluted was the upper Hudson River, according to Rockefeller's report. Albany, Troy, Utica, and other cities had contributed the sewage which prompted local residents to refer to the area as "the Albany cesspool." Now, with the announcement of Rockefeller's program, cities such as Troy had an opportunity to clean up the mess they had created. Troy, faced with a $10 million construction bill, would have to raise only $4 million. "They would never have been able to do the job on their own," a Rockefeller aide said. With the bond proposal came a stiffening of the state's attitude toward polluters. When Troy's city officials showed little concern for the damage it had done to the river, one state attorney said New York would do everything in its power to force Troy to get on with construction plans "even if it means stopping up every sewer in town."

It is on this point that the success of Rockefeller's plan to clean up the state ultimately depends. The billion-dollar bond issue, for all its virtue, remains a cure rather than a preventative. The money will build plants to treat the filth which is being poured into the streams faster than the plants can cope with it. One bond issue will simply lead to another. After listening to Rockefeller express his fears to a congressional committee that a "tough" policy would drive paper plants and other industry from the state, Representative Richard D. McCarthy of New York responded with a striking illustration.

"Another point, Governor, you mentioned the paper plants," McCarthy said. "Well, a company that I just left to come here has a paper plant at Newburgh, New York, and you alluded to something that I sympathize with you on. You do not want to force them out of business. However, I think it is interesting that in my company at Pryor, Oklahoma; Anniston, Alabama; and Kalamazoo, Michigan, to name just three, we have other paper plants, and in each of those localities we were obliged, under strict enforcement, to stop producing our effluents into the streams. And we did not move those plants out of there. But we were never—nothing was ever alleged against us at Newburgh, New York. I do not think industry is irresponsible when the laws are enforced. Certainly in our case at Pryor, Anniston, and Kalamazoo, we complied, but there was never any effort to bring us into compliance at Newburgh."

Having set about curing the patient, the state must now attack the disease.

Nine: The Cost of Water Pollution

I

> Such water do the gods distil,
> And pour down every hill
>   For their New England men;
> A draught of this wild nectar bring
> And I'll not taste the spring
>   Of helicon again.

Henry David Thoreau dedicated these lines to the Merrimack River, on which he and his brother traveled in 1839 in a boat they had made with their own hands. "I have traced its stream from where it bubbles out of the rocks of the White Mountains above the clouds," he wrote, "to where it is lost amid the salt billows of the ocean on Plum Island beach." Yet already there is a shadow cast on Thoreau's god-distilled waters, for he notices the manufacturing towns on each successive plateau as the river falls in a "silver cascade" to the sea. The extent to which Thoreau's forebodings were valid was not completely realized until 1963. At that time the Merrimack had been frighteningly polluted for more than two generations. An engineering survey ordered by the Massachusetts State Legislature then disclosed that the river's pollution, composed of 54 percent industrial and 46 percent domestic wastes, had become an enormous burden to the state's people. Polluted, the Merrimack remained a menace to their health. To clean it up and restore it as a recreational asset would cost the taxpayers, the engineering report estimated, $94,575,000.

Those debts we incur because of a wasteful action are the bitterest to pay. A special attitude about waste was developed among the settlers of our country as they sought to make order out of the confusing plenitude of its natural resources. Forests were burned, wild animals were slaughtered; of the high mortality among pioneer women, William Carlos Williams has written, "The first ones died shooting children against the wilderness like cannon balls." As the smokestacks of industry replaced the forests along our rivers, the prime use of a river was decreed to be sewage disposal, an appropriation of our national assets excused by the celebrators of the American Dream as an optimistic aspect of *laissez-faire*. To characterize this attitude toward our resources as "optimistic" is perverse. It is profoundly pessimistic. The conversion of a lovely lake or a clear stream into a sewer in order to make a few dollars is the most despairing act one can imagine.

A false economy, rather than *laissez-faire*, impelled

communities to foul their rivers. If one examines waste treatment from the aspect of its tonnage, it is by far the biggest business in the United States. Yet communities have diverted only paltry sums for this immense task. The responsibility for treating a city's wastes has often been given to men who had no conception of its complexities, men akin to those "park commissioners" who feel improvements have been made when birds and greenery are rooted out and replaced by deserts of cement.

"We only need to look at the Middle East or China," Wisconsin's Senator Gaylord Nelson has said, "and you see what happens to a country which goes ahead and destroys its assets, its water and soil, its forests and scenic beauty. When they are through they have nothing left. And all across this country now, we are destroying all of these assets at a rate accelerated much more rapidly than any other country in the history of the world. And among them is water."

Americans already have paid heavily for the introduction of *laissez-faire* and pants-pocket economics into the management of their waterways. Towns are blighted by pollution. It becomes unpleasant to live in them, and people are tempted to move away. Speaking of Moodna Creek, which runs past his upstate New York home, an Air Force officer said recently, "I'd have to say the smell from that water is so bad, so strong, that it can awaken you from sleep." A branch of the League of Women Voters in Beaumont, Texas, was forced to use a variety of shock treatment in its campaign to clean up the city's waters; one of its most popular slogans was, "Beaumont is beautiful, but it stinks!" Property values in such undesirable areas decline. Because the city is left with a depressed tax base, municipal services deteriorate, shabbiness abounds, and people and industries flee.

Even communities which once boasted of adequate sewage-treatment plants find themselves in difficulty when local authorities and industrialists begin to cut corners. Some cities, reluctant to expand their plants, try to save money by forcing local industries to treat their wastes, then pile in extra raw sewage of their own. Others permit their waterways to become so degraded that water-using industries refuse to settle there. (Many industries, including those which produce beer, soft drinks, and canned vegetables, require extremely pure water and find that even the potable supply of cities affected by pollution does not meet their standards.) In these cases it is often the citizens themselves who allow their community to decline by default. David B. Lee, a Florida sanitary engineer, has recalled a striking instance.

"I had the unhappy experience recently to talk to a professor of sanitary engineering who was opposed to an annexation issue because it would cost him money," Lee said. "His septic tank, which does not function because of the location of his home, has a relief pipe into a storm drain, and so dumps raw sewage into an open waterway. Yet he is a good professor of sanitary engineering technology."

Lee might have added, however, that the professor is very poor in economics. To delay sewage construction adds finally to its cost. Sewage-treatment facilities, estimated to cost $22 million in New York City after World War II, actually cost over $80 million because of inflationary prices for labor and material during the 1960's.

Water pollution consumes tax money which might

more profitably be spent elsewhere. In New York City, where a copious supply of Hudson River water flowing past the city is normally shunned because of pollution, the authorities must pipe in water from as far as the Delaware River Basin, 70 miles away. Water mains and aqueducts are as expensive as sewer pipes, and their costs are included in the high taxes that New Yorkers pay. In other areas, some chemical wastes refuse to break down under treatment, and, indeed, interfere with the treatment of ordinary wastes. The consequent inefficient operation of the plant pushes up costs.

Often the stinginess of state and federal authorities puts an extra burden on communities. The citizens of Thomaston, Maine, balked at providing treatment for their wastes in 1965 because the state had refused to contribute substantially to the costs; Thomaston residents reasoned that the state prison, located there, was a major source of sewage. A little earlier, a special session of the Maine State Legislature quickly disposed of 60 bills before it, yet granted only $400,000 for sewage-disposal projects throughout the state. The Water Improvement Commission had asked for $1 million. "What are we supposed to do?" asked one town manager. "Build a plant with trading stamps?" Federal officials, too, have often set a poor example. Government installations polluting the Hudson River were excused by officials on the grounds that "they were only following local custom." Similarly, when federal installations were charged with being "gross polluters" of San Francisco Bay, officials blamed Congress because it had made no appropriations for sewage treatment.

Since the *laissez-faire* basis of water pollution is increasingly questioned, industry has resorted to the plea that the construction of treatment facilities at their plants is not economical. James M. Quigley, an Assistant Secretary of Health, Education and Welfare, has challenged this attitude as well. "You're going to have to recognize that pollution control is a necessary part of running a business," he told a group of manufacturers in 1964. "It is a legitimate part of your overhead." A few enlightened industrialists are finally beginning to admit that pollution is not only injurious to a community: industry itself loses money. A Scott Paper Company official has said that most plants now discharge valuable chemicals as well as water to neighboring streams. Sound economics would seem to dictate that industry separate these chemicals from its effluent, thereby converting them from harmful stream pollutants to a profitable commodity.

Enlightenment may bring with it other advantages. Congressman John A. Blatnik has said, "Industry opposition to federal pollution control legislation is shortsighted in view of industry's great need for water. Industry should cease its opposition to federal grants to municipalities, especially in view of industry's support of tax benefits for themselves for the construction of industrial treatment facilities." It seems incredible that Blatnik or any other legislator must point out to industry the advantages that will accrue to it from a supply of clean water; pollution is a drain on everyone's pocketbook.

If Eastern rivers have been turned into sewers, Western rivers are giant irrigation ditches. As such they are jealously guarded in those enormous areas which receive a light rainfall. Water, irrigating a field, picks up quantities of minerals from the soil. Returning eventually to the waterways, it carries these salts with them. Added to the natural pollution which enters the West's rivers all the time in the form of runoffs from the fields (field runoffs are estimated to contribute 13,000 tons of common salt a day to the Arkansas River), the salts picked up by irrigating waters pose extraordinary problems to water engineers. Salts create "hard" water, which requires a great deal of soap to form lather, and which may corrode pipes, boilers, and other water containers. Dallas residents during a 1955-56 water shortage bought drinking water in milk cartons rather than touch the salty river water available nearby.

The salinity of the Colorado River brought about a minor international crisis which was only solved in 1965 by an agreement between the United States and Mexico. Gathering salts from irrigated fields in the United States, the Colorado reached Mexico highly "polluted." It destroyed Mexican crops when it was used for irrigation, and was worthless for any other purpose. After repeated protests by Mexico, the United States agreed to build a channel that will divert during times of high salinity the drainage from Arizona's Wellton-Mohawk Irrigation District to the Gulf of Mexico. The United States will then control, by a series of dams, the water in the Colorado during the rest of the year so that Mexico will continue to receive at least the minimum amount of water guaranteed it by a United States-Mexico treaty. The 13-mile drainage channel will cost the United States $5 million.

Elsewhere we have seen how pesticides, oil, acid mine drainage, and even the ordinary industrial and domestic wastes of the Raritan Bay area have destroyed America's priceless wildlife. The destruction continues. Pollution off the Georgia coast has forced the state to close 74 areas (comprising 47,000 acres) to shellfishing; the state will lose $6 million a year in sales. In 1964 it was estimated that almost a million acres of clam- and oyster-producing areas in America had been lost to pollution. Laboratory studies have revealed that young Atlantic salmon, when exposed to very small amounts of DDT, choose temperatures as much as 25 degrees higher than their usual habitat. This discovery indicated that pesticides may change the migration habits of fish, with an attendant upheaval in the fishing industry. (It is not a far-fetched possibility. Rachel Carson, in *The Sea Around Us,* described how a natural change in the temperature of the water off northern Europe caused a shift in the movements of herring and altered the economic and political history of Europe.)

If pollution does not always change the habits of fish populations, it causes heavy destruction among them. In several lakes in New York's Adirondack region, all of the newly-hatched trout died when DDT permeated the yolk sacs. The Chicago *Sun-Times,* commenting recently on water pollution, cited its effect on such enormously popular recreations as fishing. "The simple truth is that fishing in the Midwest at least has been dropping off for several years, except for a few isolated places," the *Sun-Times* editorial said. "Biologists and conservation officials have been sweeping this under the rug for years." Again, an economic loss is compounded by a menace to the public health: while insects proliferate in polluted waters, schools of fish that originally controlled them have diminished.

Much wildlife destruction is the result of one government agency working at cross-purposes to another. The Department of Agriculture may use excessive amounts of spray in one area, killing wildlife that has been carefully nurtured by the Department of the Interior. The area of fish and wildlife habitat destroyed each year by water pollution is greater than that created by all public agencies conducting fish and wildlife restoration programs. Eric Sevareid, the news commentator, has spoken of "the insane contradiction in government policies. Hunters' organizations and conservationists struggle and pay great sums, private and public, for more refuges, while other government agencies pay public money to farmers of the north central states to drain their marshes and sloughs in order to grow more of the crops already in embarrassing surplus."

II

Mrs. Robert Farlow of Pennsylvania's League of Women Voters has told the story of a neighbor frantically calling the family doctor. "My child has been playing in a polluted stream," she told him. "What shall I do?"

"Spank him," the doctor said.

Children often go out of their way to find trouble, but most of us find that water pollution, and all its troubles, are right at our doorstep. It blights our communities, mars our vacations, and in a thousand ways costs us money. It also makes a great many people ill. There is no great fuss about the illnesses as a rule. They are minor gastric disturbances caused by impurities in our drinking water, and few of them are reported to the authorities. But serious illness and epidemics lie just beneath the surface of our polluted streams, causing anxiety among health authorities and demanding constant vigilance by those charged with purifying water supplies. A recent staff report from the Senate's Committee on Public Works suggests the menace posed by new chemicals.

"While the concentrations found thus far have no apparent significance from the standpoint of acute toxicity to humans as drinking water contaminants," the report says, "as the use of these chemicals increases, chronic effects of their long-term ingestion may well be of greater significance than acute toxicity."

The problem is not endemic to the United States. Jean Boyer, Professor of Hygiene at the Paris Faculty of Medicine, recently said that the entire Paris water supply is unfit to drink. The supply, he charged, contains many disease-bearing organisms, including carcinogenic substances. While their potency is low, he said that their "regular absorption is worrying us." A Scotsman complained at the same time that the water at Inverness is so foul that it "contaminates the whiskey."

But the United States, with its vast industrial and agricultural production, pours dangerous chemicals into the water at an unprecendented rate. Cases in which these chemicals have continued to multiply in "food chains" have long been documented. At Green Bay, Wisconsin, for instance, fish eaten by gulls contained in their fat one part per million of DDT; yet later the gulls were examined and found to contain 2,700 parts per million. Human beings stand (fortunately in most cases) at the end of the food chain. Writing in *The Farm Quarterly*, Alan Linn pointed out our present predicament. The average American is two pounds overweight, chiefly because of our tremendous food production, and that production in turn is made possible chiefly by the widespread use of insecticides. Concluding, Linn says, "It is one of the great ironies of our civilization that some of these chemicals are stored in the very body fat they make possible."

Another ironic fact of life is that water, a principal source of life, proves in many cases to be a source of disease. Workers in sewage-treatment plants are reportedly subject to leptosposis and infectious hepatitis. Heart disease has been linked to certain solids in drinking water. Typhoid fever has been contracted from eating watercress sandwiches. Dr. Walter L. Mellmann, Professor of Bacteriology at Michigan State University, discovered heavy concentrations of streptococcus bacteria in chlorinated swimming pools. (He noted these concentrations only when the pools were crowded with swimmers. Investigating further, he found that they came from the human respiratory system. Washed from noses and mouths into the water, the bacteria remained alive in the chlorinated water long enough to be picked up through the noses and mouths of other swimmers.)

Even greater dangers lurk in polluted waters. During a mass oral poliomyelitis immunization program in Ohio, samples of water were collected from the Ohio River and local primary treatment plants. According to the Public Health Service report, "Virus was present in considerable quantities in sewage five days after initial vaccine administration. Virus continued to be detected in some quantity in sewage nine months after the last dose of vaccine was administered. A total of 139 of the 157 virus strains recovered have been identified as of the three polio-virus types."

Occasionally a dreaded disease breaks through. When

an epidemic begins, it is again only the vigilance of public health authorities that restricts even more widespread misery. Perhaps no case in modern times more clearly demonstrates the ease with which faulty sewage facilities can spread disease than the typhoid epidemic which was carried from a rural encampment to 15 different states during 1956.

On August 23 of that year, the Louisiana Department of Health reported a curious discovery to the United States Public Health Service. Two people, living in widely separated communities in the state, had contracted typhoid fever. A routine investigation turned up two interesting facts which seemed to be more than coincidence. Both victims belonged to the same religious sect, and both had attended a conference at an encampment belonging to the sect at Monark Springs, Missouri, late in July. The report evoked the same response from every official who read it. Without waiting for further reports, the PHS notified the Missouri Department of Public Health and began a search for every person who had attended the religious conference.

An inquiry to church leaders brought the information that there had been 550 people at the conference. Most of them had come from Missouri and Oklahoma, though 15 states, extending from Pennsylvania to California and Oregon, were listed. Health authorities in each of these states were alerted, and asked to obtain stool specimens from the people who might be infected. Soon the reports began to come in. More than half of the conference's participants had had diarrhea while at Monark Springs. Some of them were already seriously ill. One person had died of typhoid fever.

Now that all of the participants who had been located were under medical attention, or were being carefully watched, federal and state health authorities turned their attention to the campsite at Monark Springs. Located in southwestern Missouri, it was a typically rustic encampment in an area of limestone rock, where dormitories, cabins, and tenting space had been provided for visitors. The Public Health Service report describes its sanitary facilities: "A 180-foot drilled well, located near the center of the camp, supplied water to several buildings through an underground pipe system. For many years, two pit privies had provided the only toilet facilities on the campsite. During the winter before the 1956 meeting, a sewage-disposal system with 12 flush toilets, a large unsealed septic tank and open-end underground drainage field was installed. The well was slightly down hill from the septic tank and sewage drainage area."

The campers arrived on a Friday. Over the weekend there were especially heavy rains so that by Sunday the drinking water had become cloudy. A day or two later it had acquired a distinctly unpleasant taste, and its appearance was later described by members of the religious group as like "soapy dishwater" and "sewage." They finally refused to touch it, and fresh water was then brought from town. Following this lead, health authorities satisfied their suspicions about the well. By this time the water had cleared up (no one had been using the campsite) so a green dye was dropped into the camp's toilets. Less than 18 hours later the well water itself turned green. The investigators had proved that sewage seeped from the septic tank to the well.

And then the last link in the investigation fell into

place. It came in the report on a 41-year-old woman who had suffered a minor diarrheal illness during the conference. This woman was one of the unfortunates known in the medical world as a "carrier." She had contracted typhoid fever in 1940. Like about five percent of those who eventually recover from the disease, she continued to nourish typhoid bacilli in her system. (The famous "Typhoid Mary", a New York housemaid, infected over 50 people in that city earlier in the century before she was finally traced as the disease's carrier.) The woman at Monark Springs had been recognized as a carrier in her local district and, like all known carriers, had been prohibited from handling the food of other people and engaging in work through which she might easily pass on the disease. Under ordinary circumstances she might have led an unruffled life, for typhoid is transmitted only through food and drink contaminated by the excreta of its victims. Sewage treatment usually destroys the bacilli. When sewage treatment is absent, or when it fails, an epidemic strikes.

This is what happened at Monark Springs. There were 34 cases of typhoid eventually traced to drinking its well water, hundreds of minor intestinal illnesses and one fatality. Polluted water seldom exacts such a dramatic toll, but it is always at work around us. The cost, dramatic or unobtrusive, is invariably heavy.

Ten: An Ounce of Prevention

I

The United States remains, in its approach to waste disposal, mired in the Dark Ages. Our technology is primitive, our attitudes barbaric. The notion lingers that waste disposal is one of the proper uses of a stream, and apparently the *only* proper use of a good many streams. This is nonsense. To degrade or destroy a body of water cannot be putting it to its best use. Expedience has forced us to pour our sewage into neighboring waterways but we should not consider this a permanent solution. At the moment, we are being overwhelmed by our own wastes—wastes which pollute our waters, poison our air, and make dumping grounds of our roadsides. Until we have learned how to eliminate or to make use of these wastes we can hardly lay claim to being civilized. In diligent and imaginative scientific research lies our best hope. In the meanwhile, it is up to the people of this nation (who presumably control their own destiny) to mitigate by law and the proper enforcement of that law the present ravages of pollution.

The problem is not hopeless. Somehow in the past man's better instincts have suppressed his greed just enough to allow him to survive within his environment. There have been close calls, and there will be closer ones as the deadliest animal refines his devices for murder and suicide. No matter how estranged he has grown from his environment, man still cannot live without water. He is fouling that indispensable resource. Why must it always be one hairbreadth escape after another?

We have looked into the Missouri, the Mississippi, and the Hudson rivers, Raritan Bay and the Great Lakes, and have come away suitably depressed. Those turbid depths are but a reflection of the universal condition of our waters: in his 1965 State of the Union message, President Johnson reported that every major river system in this country is polluted. We have described the mass of domestic, industrial, and chemical wastes which overburden our streams. We might have talked at length about the natural salts which sterilize our Western rivers, and the radioactive wastes which lately have found their way into so many of our waterways. We might also have included heat among our most destructive pollutants, for much of the water which cools the machinery of industry is poured steaming hot back into the rivers (temperatures in West Virginia's Mahoning River near industrial areas have been recorded at over 105 degrees); the overheated water, its ability diminished to hold oxygen in solution, is rendered less capable of assimilating oxygen-demanding wastes, and pollution builds up geometrically. Every river tells its sordid story.

Rivers, which should be among America's glories, have become instead its sewers, and every level of society has ignored its obligation to them. Where do we begin if we are to reverse the disastrous process of disintegration? Clearly, the impetus must come from the country as a whole, from that "public" which has lost touch with the sources of its life in Nature and let its most vital natural resource fall by default to the exploiters. Unaffiliated citizens are invited to speak at many of the conferences and meetings at which water problems are discussed. Too often, however, the crackpots and the publicity seekers are the only ones to raise their voices. Similarly, when pollution control boards are set up, industry presses for heavy representation while the public at large is silent and its representation consequently is light. The public's pressure on legislators, either at the state or the federal level, has been equally spotty. State legislators, especially, have neither the staffs nor the time to help them acquaint themselves with all the aspects of pending legislation, and so they remain open to the propaganda of groups with economic motives. These groups actually write much of our present legislation and the "lawmakers" simply ratify it. The result, as R. G. Lynch, a Wisconsin newspaperman, has said, is that "Laws generally put private rights ahead of public rights and emphasize economic uses, to the detriment and sometimes the exclusion of public uses."

Conservation organizations have given the concerned citizen a reasonably effective base from which to make his fears and desires known to legislators; there is, after all, strength in numbers. Yet these organizations, usually staffed by dedicated men and women, are not as effective as the staffs of lobbyists employed by the polluting industrial organizations. Industries may charge off the considerable costs of an efficient lobby to business expenses, using money which would otherwise by paid to the government in taxes. Conservation organizations, generally short of money to begin with, are hampered by federal law. Citizens may deduct from their income taxes contributions to educational organizations such as the National Audubon Society and the Izaac Walton League; yet these organizations may not devote more than "an insubstantial amount" of their funds to influence legislation, under penalty of losing their tax status. "An insubstantial amount" is interpreted so strictly by the Internal Revenue Service that most educational groups refrain even from advising their members by mail to write their congressmen about pollution legislation.

If the people have failed individually, their cause has not been very much advanced by either their local or state governments. Municipal authorities are notorious laggards. In 1914 the Ohio State Board of Health ordered Cleveland to stop polluting "forthwith" the Cuyahoga River. Studies of water samples taken by the Cleveland *Press* 50 years later proved that the river's quality had been further degraded during that time, prompting the newspaper to speak of Cleveland's "sweep it under the rug" policy.

In recent years a state government here and there has tried to cast off the delusionary notion that it works hand in glove with industry to provide clean streams for happy people; in the main, however, state programs seem prompted more by a fear that the federal government will step in than by any clear conviction that the job needs to be done. After the Public Health Service had been looking into the mess at Lake Michigan for several years, Governor Otto Kerner of Illinois and Governor Matthew Welsh of Indiana suddenly decided in the fall of 1964 that they must take some action. They met hastily and agreed to "crack down" on polluters. "Rather than have the federal government move in, we'll have the states act now," one of Kerner's aides said. The PHS report issued the following spring in Chicago (and corroborated by Chicago officials) revealed how meager the states' action had been.

Even where the will to act has shown itself as more than a reflexive spasm, state measures against water pollution are generally ineffective. Their legislatures allot paltry subsidies for staffs, equipment, and research. A sample of the kind of reports turned in by state officials is that of the Texas Water Pollution Control Board after its survey of polluted Galveston Bay in 1964. It noted that there had been "no significant deterioration" since 1951. To avert a final disaster is, in the state's eyes, to achieve success. Other states try to function under obsolete laws. In Alabama, the water pollution control law passed in 1949 effected only new industries, exempting those which were in existence at the time. Ira L. Myers, chief of the Alabama Water Improvement Commission, said recently that "water discharged from those industries exempt from control because of the so-called 'Grandfather Clause' is a major cause of the industrial pollution of Alabama's waters."

Yet many state officials refuse to acknowledge what has happened. The legislative assistant to a United States

Senator tells of a visit he made several years ago to a Midwestern state. "I took a tour along the shores of a river that is notoriously polluted," he says, "and I happened to come on a fish kill. There was a state conservation official there and I asked him what had happened. He looked out at the river very seriously and he said, 'Those fish died of lack of oxygen.' I almost laughed in his face. It was as if a detective found a body full of bullet holes and refused to look for a murderer because the victim had died of loss of blood."

There is some genuine concern among state officials that federal intervention in water pollution cases may generate certain abuses. "Take the case of the federal government classifying state waters," an aide to Governor Rockefeller says. "What you do about classifying waters determines the economics of an entire region. Suppose a certain administration wanted to punish a state for its opposition to that administration's views? Suppose, say, a liberal President wanted to punish a segregationist state like Mississippi? What better way than to have its waters classified so that no industry could survive there!"

But generally the fierce resentment of government intervention originates in the petty jealousy of state officials who have not been able to cope with an enormous problem. When this resentment comes to the surface, we are treated to the sort of spectacle which marred an attempt to clean up New England's waters several years ago: sulking officials from Maine and New Hampshire refused to take part as conferees in a conference called by the Public Health Service (but at a second session of the conference participated from seats in the audience).

The jealousy of state officials is gleefully fed by industrial spokesmen who manipulate states' rights for their own economic ends. "Big Government" is pictured as a particularly dangerous kind of bogeyman. *The New Republic's* columnist, TRB, commented on these industrial spokesmen in 1964: ". . . there is an amusing similarity between them and Marxists who believe that ultimately government will wither completely away. Many of those who ardently shouted 'states' rights' . . . have had, I believe, an ulterior interest in preserving privilege or halting progress; they knew that state legislatures were more easily bought and sold than the Federal government. Maybe it's unfortunate, but about the only counterweight the little man has to Big Business is Big Government; the record of the century is that business has grown big first, and that government has come limping along behind."

Before a 1963 hearing of the House Subcommittee on Government Operations, Hill R. Healan of the Georgia Association of County Commissioners was asked if his state had a regulatory agency in the field of water pollution.

"Yes, sir," Healan replied. "Unfortunately, we do not have the kinds of laws necessary to do it. We have a water resources commission which is part of the state health department. Here is what they do, actually, under existing law: someone will come in from the state and make a complaint about what he thinks would be a pollution problem. They will meet and hear the complaint. That is about the extent of it."

Healan went on to say that he thought the most urgent need was to make the public aware of the vastness of the problem. Until a state education program became generally effective, Healan despaired of making any progress against the polluters. "The reason we took this approach is that we had, that I know of, three legislative committees set up to study the problem," he said. "They would make the study, point out the dangers, and make the reports. And then a feeble effort made in the general assembly to get the necessary laws would be beaten down by the polluters."

As awareness spreads of the enormous job to be done, there seems to be also at last the recognition that enormous resources will be required to do it. On the way toward asking federal assistance many states have entered into interstate compacts, using a regional river basin as a unifying force. These compacts generally set water standards for the basin and facilitate the exchange of information among the states. But, since interstate agencies, like the state agencies, are under the legal and financial thumb of state legislatures, there is little inclination within them to enforce their regulations. As one state official has said, "Most of these agencies are a sort of informal confessional, where one state gets together with another and they tell each other their troubles."

It is generally admitted that the only reasonably effective interstate compact is the Ohio River Valley Water Sanitation Compact (popularly known as ORSANCO). Formed in 1948 by the states of Ohio, Indiana, Illinois, Kentucky, New York, West Virginia, Pennsylvania, and Virginia, its stated purpose is to "place and maintain the waters in a satisfactory sanitary condition." The strong hand behind ORSANCO was Ohio's Senator Robert A. Taft, who was able to place representatives of the federal government in the organization, along with those of the member states.

"When states get together they seem to want to oust the federal government instead of making use of it," Alabama's Congressman Robert E. Jones says. "Senator Taft was able to make the federal government really an interested party in ORSANCO. For that reason it has been one of the finest that we have had."

ORSANCO has made an effort to do the job, monitoring the quality of the river, tracing sources of pollution, and taking color motion pictures from the air to convince polluters of their guilt. Edward Cleary, its executive director, is a tireless worker, even watching the Ohio River with binoculars during spare moments at his home on Cincinnati's Eastwood Drive. "Many boat operators wonder why they are cited for violations as they pass a certain point on the river," he told a Cincinnati *Enquirer* reporter. "They don't realize I have my glasses on them when they enter the local pool."

The opposition to all interstate compacts has been summed up by Charles Callison, who was appointed to the Federal Water Pollution Advisory Board by the late President Kennedy and is now assistant to the president of the National Audubon Society. "What is the United States Constitution but an interstate compact?" he asked. "But these are 'bastard' compacts, odd, unnatural growths on the body politic. The river basin plan is good river management but it is not logical politically. These agencies still have to go begging to the state legislatures for their funds.

"The interstate compact approach has never exhibited exceptional vigor nor demonstrated unusual achievement in the abatement of water pollution," Callison continued. "ORSANCO and the Interstate Sanitation Commission for the New York metropolitan region have both distinguished themselves more for the issuance of soothing syrup to the public than for cracking down on recalcitrant polluters. The New England Interstate Water Pollution Control Commission has been a flat failure, as any objective look at the polluted streams of that region will disclose. These interstate agencies characteristically stress the reasonableness of their policies and methods, and the years stretch into decades of inaction."

Another distinguished conservationist, the late Kenneth A. Reid, felt the same way. Writing in the *Iowa Conservationist* back in 1948, Reid recalled that interstate compacts "have been strongly advocated by those desiring to avoid Federal control. In theory they are fine but in practice they don't work. In spite of all the fanfare on interstate compacts, and particularly the Ohio Valley compact which has been many years in the making, if you will examine the wording you will find that they contain the veto power which nullifies all their other fine mandatory declarations against pollution. They are, in effect, another means or method of stalling off the Federal control that will inevitably be necessary to get the job on pollution done."

Assistant Secretary of Health, Education and Welfare James Quigley has said it bluntly: "Pollution control is an activity which in the final analysis depends upon the police power." In many cases it would be most desirable if local and state governments assumed the enforcement powers themselves. Some areas have taken revolutionary steps, as Florida's Dade County did when it banned the sale of hard detergents there after a stipulated date, adding to the minimal pressure then being applied to reluctant detergent manufacturers by Washington. In 1964 West Virginia hardened its attitude toward polluters. Using its new pollution law, the state fined DuPont's plant at Belle, West Virginia, $40,568 for "accidentally spilling" chemicals into the Kanawha River. The chemicals, chiefly ammonia, had killed thousands of fish.

Obviously the people on the scene can be more effective in tracking down the specific sources of pollution. After numberless complaints from residents along New York's Moodna Creek, the state health department finally took action against the Frost White Mills, a paper-manufacturing plant, which was generally known to be the creek's major polluter. (The hearing had aroused so much interest in that upper New York State region that it was broadcast over a Newburgh radio station.) At the last minute the plant's attorney, admitting that his client had polluted the creek, tried unsuccessfully to have the hearing cancelled. According to a story in the New York *Daily News*, the attorney "appeared flushed and angry at the proceedings, having claimed that, since the mill operators had admitted to the pollution, the hearing was only an attempt to embarrass the owners." There can be no more efficient way to clean up a stream than by "embarrassing" the polluters with a public recital of the odious mess they have created.

Vigorous state courts can play their role in pollution abatement too. When the town of Waterford, New York, refused to build a sewage-treatment plant on the grounds that it could not afford one, the state court of appeals dismissed its argument. The court's ruling said that the town's defense "is another way of saying that a physician may not diagnose a serious disease as such if the patient cannot afford the cost of cure . . . The legislature well knew that a comprehensive water purification program would impose a financial burden upon the municipalities of the State, but determined, by enacting the Pollution Control Act, that the pressing need for water purification outweighed any financial hardships incident thereto."

Yet, despite the most vigorous local and state action, there is a point past which only the federal government can go. To protect responsible industries that have done their share to treat their wastes, yet operate at a competitive disadvantage against those who have cut costs by evading their obligations to the community; to protect communities and states against industries which threaten to move away if compelled to obey the law; and to protect the people in "clean" states from evil-smelling, disease-bearing water passed on to them from "dirty" states: these are inevitably federal responsibilities. Here is corroborative testimony from a 1964 issue of *The Louisiana Conservationist:* "Brines from South Arkansas oil fields had been a source of pollution for northern Louisiana streams and lakes for years, but this condition has improved tremendously in the past four years and will continue to do so. The change resulted from the first interstate enforcement action ever taken by the United States Public Health Service in stream pollution."

II

The federal government, like some fabled giant, embodies a curious mixture of strengths and weaknesses: a long reach negated by a tendency toward myopia; awesome power tempered by sluggish reflexes; and a generous disposition curdled by the mistrust its size seems to evoke. This giant's weaknesses are only too apparent, and too easily exploited. Its congressmen are often obtuse, sometimes venal. Its various departments are bogged down in bureaucracy, all so incapable of seeing past their own immediate concerns that a great deal of energy is wasted, unknowingly or otherwise, in tripping each other up. Yet here, whether we like it or not, stands America's best defense against the rising tide of water pollution.

This statement must be based on the government's potential, not on its accomplishments. We have noted a few cases (and there are many more) where one arm of the government was trying to clean up a certain stream while another was dumping into it raw pollution as unconcernedly as a Nebraska packer. Murray Stein, in his enforcement duties, has been frustrated as often by other federal employees as by the most jealous state stream-control official. "So many government departments and agencies are schizoid in character," Stein says. "On the one hand they are supposed to regulate certain industries, and on the other they are supposed to help them. In the end they become a sort of lobby for the industry they should regulate."

The Atomic Energy Commission doubles as an apologist for those who contaminate waterways with radioactive wastes. The Department of the Interior, appointed guardian of America's wildlife, also must promote the interests of the same mine operators whose acid drainage kills off the fish in nearby streams. The Department of Agriculture's position as an advocate of the farmer prompted its Secretary, Orville Freeman, to attack Secretary of the Interior Stewart Udall's suggestion that those pesticides be prohibited which run off the fields to poison streams. ("Too little is known," was Freeman's reason for moving cautiously, to which *The New Yorker* magazine replied, "The Freeman doctrine appears to be that the less you know about a poison the freer you should feel to use it.")

The Public Health Service has come in for more than its share of criticism because of its management of the federal water pollution program. The program is centered in a division within PHS, relatively insignificant in proportion to the enormity of the problem. "The program is run by doctors," one conservationist says. "They look into pollution just long enough to make sure that nobody is dying of it, and then they leave it alone. They don't give a hoot for wildlife or any other values." In other quarters the complaint is heard that the doctors prefer to "advise," rather than to involve themselves with controversial enforcement action, an attitude which *The New Republic* says leads to "foot-dragging." Congressman John Dingell has been a critic of the PHS for a long time. He feels that it has "not been vigorous or forceful in its actions in abating pollution," and that the Taft Sanitary Engineering Center in Cincinnati, established for further research on water problems, has become "crammed with all imaginable forms of activities." The Center, Dingell says, "is used for research in air pollution, radiological health, environmental engineering and food protection, and occupational health in addition to water pollution control. This is an example, in my opinion, of where the Public Health Service has frankly sacrificed the resources of its pollution abatement program to other interests, and this is a very bad thing."

Whenever the Public Health Service performs its job well, however, it is immediately criticized by people who feel that the truth will cost them money. Art Buchwald, Washington's satirical columnist, has poked fun at the big industrial lobbies there. In 1964 he noted that "one of the most important jobs that public relations men in Washington are expected to fulfill is to deny the accuracy of a government report." He sketched for his readers an imaginary scene after the Mississippi fish kill. A press agent handed him a release. "Read it. Our people made a study which showed that pesticides actually helped the fish. It killed the germs on them. Not one of those fish died from yellow fever."

Part of the fault for the confusion and timidity within the federal government's pollution program must be attributed to Congress. It had never passed a water pollution control bill until 1948, and did not set up a permanent program until 1956. During the remainder of the Eisenhower administration there was no further progress in pollution legislation. A new version of the 1956 bill was vetoed by the President in 1960. Those who persistently look for sinister motives, behind action as well as inaction, thought they detected the influence of the President's former assistant, Sherman Adams, in this veto; a New Englander, Adams' sympathies were identified with the region's paper and textile mills. It is more likely, however, that Eisenhower was simply adhering to his own notions of government economy. Pollution control is notoriously expensive.

The Federal Water Pollution Control Act was strengthened by the amendments written into it under the Kennedy Administration in 1961. Federal enforcement authority was broadened, and additional funds were set aside for research and local treatment-plant construction.* It was felt at the time by certain optimistic conservationists that the next steps toward clean water would be a great deal easier now because of the apparently favorable climate which had allowed these amendments to be passed by Congress. Events since 1961, however, prove that the struggle is still a bitter one. The road to more effective anti-pollution laws has been obstructed by both the delaying tactics of industry and the internecine struggle among the various factions advocating clean streams.

This struggle within "the movement" has some fascinating aspects. One issue which was expected to be extremely controversial has, for the moment, been settled. This has to do with the proper seat of federal pollution regulation. By 1965 almost everybody had agreed that the logical step was to remove this responsibility from the Public Health Service and set up an agency to be called the Federal Water Pollution Control Administration under a new Assistant Secretary of Health, Education and Welfare. The proposed agency would have more scope and prestige than the old Water Pollution Control division, buried within PHS; it would, for instance, be akin to the Food and Drug Administration. Some Washington observers, inclined to speculation, believe this step will be followed by the transfer of water pollution control entirely from HEW to the Department of the Interior.

* A summary of major federal water pollution legislation can be found in the Appendix.

"This was really a tempest in a teapot," one old Washington hand says. "Not many people realized it but water pollution control was technically taken away from the Public Health Service in 1961. When the act was amended, every place where the Surgeon General had been mentioned in the original 1956 act was changed to read the Secretary of HEW. The people who wrote the amendments had prepared the way for the new agency, but the time wasn't ripe for it then."

The speculation that pollution regulation will eventually be transferred to the Department of the Interior is without much substance at this time. In the best of circumstances it is extremely difficult to take away any of the responsibilities of a cabinet member, which the Secretary of HEW happens to be; Harold L. Ickes discovered this rather painfully under the New Deal when he tried to appropriate certain functions of the Department of Agriculture for his own Interior Department. The best chance of affecting such a transfer would seem to be at the outset of a new administration before the President has appointed his cabinet. A prospective secretary, his appointment hinging on certain stipulations, would be more likely to agree to the loss of an agency than would a secretary already entrenched.

A far stickier subject is that dealing with water-quality standards. There is one faction in the struggle for stronger water pollution legislation which believes that a set of standards, acceptable to the federal government, should be drawn up for all interstate waters; a state failing to establish such standards would be ineligible to receive federal sewage-treatment construction grants. Another faction believes that, since even the federal government does not have the staffs to police all interstate waterways, the states should first be given a chance to work out their own methods of abating pollution.

Senator Edmund Muskie of Maine, who leads the Senate drive for further pollution legislation, is the most outspoken proponent of water-quality standards in Congress. "Opposition to standards is based on a misunderstanding," Muskie says. "No one will require each stream to match every other stream in the country in purity. Each stream will be graded realistically and even stretches of the same stream will be given a different classification. You can't expect a river running through a heavily populated and industrial area to have exactly the same quality of water as an isolated mountain brook. But we must begin somewhere. When I was Governor of Maine I pushed the concept of upgrading rivers by gradually raising their standards of purity. This will give everybody a standard to go by, and it will be a big boost for state enforcement."

The leading spokesman against standards in Congress is Representative John Blatnik of Minnesota. He feels that research and technology in this field is not far enough advanced to make nationwide standards realistic. He also feels that it would overburden the federal enforcement officers. (Blatnik is a fervid admirer of Murray Stein; though the congressman's stand may reflect the feelings of the chief of enforcement, Stein himself believes the decision is up to the legislators and has not taken sides publicly on the issue.) One of Blatnik's supporters, however, has expressed some bitterness toward Muskie. "When Muskie was running for reelection to the Senate in 1964 the Administration looked around for a ball he could carry to give him more prestige," this man says. "So they let him introduce pollution legislation in the Senate. Now Muskie's campaign is over but he won't give up the ball. Water pollution is a big thing. Muskie's got standards on the brain."

Nevertheless, Senator Muskie has some strong supporters. In 1965 a Senate water pollution bill gave HEW authority to define standards of purity for all interstate streams, but Blatnik's committee in the House did not mention them. The *New York Times* called the House action "a backward step." It went on to say, "If most of the states had shown sufficient initiative, energy and good faith in the fight against pollution over the past 20 years, Federal action—except for auxiliary financial assistance—would not be needed. This is a victory for the paper, textile, steel and other industries that have been polluting the nation's rivers for decades."

According to the syndicated newspaper column "The Allen-Scott Report," Muskie received even more tangible support. Orville Freeman, the Secretary of Agriculture, who was said to have resented HEW's new powers in interstate stream control, attacked the proposal to establish water-purity standards. President Johnson, however, had been impressed by Muskie's position. When he heard of Freeman's stand, he summoned him to the White House and told him to keep out of the dispute. "The onetime Minnesota governor has painfully learned President Johnson does not take lightly having members of his cabinet engage in free-wheeling on legislation he favors," the story said. "Freeman did—and the President cracked down bluntly and forcefully . . . He hasn't said a word or lifted a finger on this issue since."

Other charges in federal pollution legislation that have

been proposed are an increase in construction grants and an allotment of funds to investigate the separation of storm and domestic sewers. "But the most far reaching extension of federal authority in these proposed amendments," Senator Muskie says, "is the one which would give the government the authority to move into a state and clean up the pollution around its shellfish areas. The basis for this amendment is that, even though these may not be interstate waters, the shellfish are a commodity in interstate commerce. They can be a threat to the public health in other states."

As members of both factions in Congress thrashed out the issue in conferences, there could be heard in other quarters a demand that Congress and state legislatures take another step toward clean streams by granting industry certain tax incentives for building its own sewage-treatment facilities. Expenses for construction could be deducted from industry taxes, and the treatment plants themselves would not be subject to real-estate taxes. Here, once again, a conflict among branches of government has slowed the struggle against pollution. While HEW would like to see these incentives given to progressive industries, the Treasury Department has so far rejected the idea, feeling it is "just another way for somebody to dodge taxes." The alternate suggestion is that industries be charged proportionately on the amount of pollution they pour into public waterways; "It is an incentive for private gain to achieve a public purpose," says one of the proponents of an "effluent charge." The idea seems to be almost without merit. The government would, in effect, give industry the choice between paying to pollute public waterways (and being able to deduct this "effluent charge" from its taxes) and actually controlling pollution by building treatment facilities. Too many industries, one can safely say after scanning the past record, would take the easy way out.

It is to be hoped that industry, as a whole, will promote the adoption of a tax incentive to abate local pollution. In the past industry has joined ranks chiefly to fight every forward step in pollution control. Is there the hint of any change in industry's attitude? For the good of the country and the preservation of its natural resources, one must hope that the individual businessman is not as rapacious as his organization generally makes him out to be. Associations of real-estate operators clamor against a new park for the people, an association of chemical manufacturers shrugs off the latest fish kill; yet the individual businessman is likely to be a man who enjoys his garden, fishes and swims, and takes delight in watching his children grow in a bright, healthy environment. Drop the same businessman into a gang (politely called a professional organization), and he runs with a pack that is as destructive as the mob of wild-eyed big-city hoodlums who race through subway trains smashing windows and tearing out seats. This comparison is not really fair, of course, to the teenage hoodlums. The windows and seats can be repaired. But our children's children will look back with distaste at the barbarians who bequeathed them a blighted, contaminated countryside.

Eleven: . . . And a Pound of Cure

David G. Stephan of the Public Health Service's Branch of Basic and Applied Science spoke recently to some visitors at his Washington office about the current research in the advanced waste treatment of water. On his desk stood four vials filled with water of varying quality. Two were badly discolored, one was rather unappetizingly cloudy, and the fourth was clear.

"Hand me that vial of tap water," Stephan asked one of his visitors.

The man reached for the vial of clear water.

"No," Dr. Stephan said, shaking his head. "I said the tap water."

The visitor hesitated and Dr. Stephan sat back and chuckled. "I try that on everybody who comes in here, and they all make the same mistake," he said. "That brownish liquid in the first two vials is water which hasn't been treated. The cloudy one is a sample we took from a drinking water tap in a big Midwestern city. The clear water you reached for is the product of an experimental advanced waste treatment plant."

That last vial on David Stephan's desk is a hopeful portent of what American science and technology may be able to bring about in pollution abatement. In fact, because the prevention of water pollution can be at best only partially successful, treated waste water of this purity will some day be a necessity. The propaganda distributed by polluters suggests that our water supply is inexhaustible because there is as much water in and around the earth today as there was thousands of years ago. As one industry publicist has said, "It is possible that some of your morning shower was used by Mother Eve to bathe Cain and Abel."

It is true that our water supply is constant, but our demands on that supply continue to increase. Americans today use 300 billion gallons of water every 24 hours. In 20 years it is said that Americans will be using twice this amount—and that is approximately the amount of fresh water which will be available to the country from every possible source! We already reuse a part of our present supply (it is estimated that the water in the Ohio River at times of low flow is used almost four times as it travels from Pennsylvania to the Mississippi). Yet under the most efficient treatment we are capable of giving this water, its quality deteriorates every time it is used. Our present methods cannot remove all the minerals, chemicals, and nutrients in the waste water; its composition changes with each use. Occasionally such great quantities of chlorine are required to purify badly polluted water that it must undergo another process to "dechlorinate" it. Some water that has been used over and over, and is still considered potable by human beings, has been found to be intolerable to plants and wildlife.

Westerners have always been acquainted with what it means to face a chronic water shortage. Though the West, by definition, makes up one half of our country, it has available to it less than one-fifth of our water. Only in certain areas there, like the Olympic Forest of the Northwest, is water plentiful. In California the supply is shared so unequally that the southern part of the state hopes to have its meager reservoirs augmented by water sent through aqueducts from the more fortunate north. In the northeastern United States a few brave voices have called the severe drought of recent years "a blessing in disguise." The drought is seen as a warning to the people of our big cities that the present acute water shortages will become a chronic condition in the future as an increasing population and industry further degrade their limited supply.

Today we must take pains to gather and conserve as much as possible of the water that falls from the skies. The annual rainfall on America is considerable (it is estimated to be about 4,300 billion gallons a day) yet only a minute fraction of this total is available to us. About 72 percent evaporates; most of the rest runs into the sea before we can retain it. Scientists believe that by prodigious engineering feats we can retain the 650 billion gallons a day which must be available to us by 1980, but that is the limit. Stopgap methods of conserving our water consumption are also limited. To install meters, for instance, and charge people on the amount of water they take is only partially successful; the use of water drops after the installation of meters in a city, but it generally rises again after a year or two.

It is obvious that our serious researchers into water problems are now running a race against time. We have been terribly slow to begin that race. There is not a single epidemiologist in the country devoting his full time to the study of water-borne diseases. We know little about the methods of breaking down each of the new chemicals that reach our treatment plants, and even less about dealing with them when they appear, as they do frequently, mingling with each other in our wastes. One great need of scientists is additional information about the composition of industry wastes, yet some industries are reluctant to release these figures on the grounds that in doing so they may reveal their "trade secrets."

Meanwhile the Public Health Service, often restricted by small staffs and paltry operating expenses, looks into the field known as "advanced waste treatment." (A good part of the PHS program is actually conducted under contract by universities and private research organizations.) The purpose of this research is to return all water, after it has been used, to our rivers in its original purity. "We can now conceive of cities and industry eventually having *dry* sewage," Dr. Stephan says.

There are two stages in this program; first the waste water must be purified, and afterwards the residue (or sludge) must be disposed of so that it is no longer a hazard. The first stage is composed of a series of treatments, akin to many of our present purification methods, in which the waste water's pollutants are removed. One process removes only part of the pollutants; more advanced processes destroy the hardier ones. Among the processes with which scientists are now working are Oxidation, Carbon Adsorption, Foaming, and Freezing. In the oxidation process, an exotic oxide literally burns up the wastes in the water. In carbon adsorption activated carbon separates organic impurities from the water, a principle used in the making of beer and gin, as well as in the modern filter cigarette. Foaming and freezing, though different techniques, produce somewhat similar results in that the impurities adhere to the foam bubbles or ice crystals; when the foam is dispersed or the crystals rinsed, the removal of impurities is nearly complete.

Although this complicated series of treatments is comparatively new, there already have been some startling results. At Whittier Narrows, near Los Angeles, an advanced waste treatment plant takes raw sewage from a trunk sewer, treats it, and returns it to the ground, where it filters into nearby wells, augmenting the local drinking-water supply. At Santee, California, sewage is run through a series of lagoons, each "polishing" the waste to a higher degree of purity, so that in the final lagoon the water is suitable for boating, swimming, and water skiing. Because this water is composed solely of sewage, undiluted by "clean" water, there was some reluctance by the local people to use it for recreation. The "aesthetic barrier" has now been broken down by the demonstrated purity of the water. Sewage treated in a similar fashion at Lake Tahoe on the California-Nevada border is pumped into a nearby river and used for irrigation. Of this reclaimed sewage one engineer has said, "The clarity of the finished product exceeds that of most surface waters and equals that of the best well water."

One problem at the moment is that the sewage may emerge "too clean." Water devoid of all its life-giving minerals is simply distilled water; scientists take pains to leave some of the valuable minerals in water which undergoes advanced waste treatment. Another problem is the high cost of such treatment. Raw waste water which receives both primary and secondary treatment now costs on the national average about 17 cents per thousand gallons. When advanced-treatment plants operate on a large scale, their costs will probably be at least three times higher than this figure. Yet all sewage-treatment costs will rise as our increasing population and industry overburden our waterways. The alternatives—unmanageably polluted streams and chronic water shortages—do not make the estimated costs prohibitive.

Although there has been a great deal of talk about desalting the sea water around us and making it a part of our drinking supply, many engineers now believe that the advanced treatment of our present waste waters is both more feasible and more economical. Sea water is actually "contaminated" to a higher degree than our waste water, its concentration of salts exceeding the concentration of sewage in our effluent, and is thus more expensive to refine. Perhaps more important is the fact that by the advanced treatment of wastes we are solving two problems in one process: we are providing ourselves with a new water supply while cleaning up our waterways.

One major question remains. What will happen to the residue from waste water which has received advanced treatment? While the treatment in most cases removes the pollutants, it does not destroy them. There is now a program of intensive research in this field, too. One solution is being tested at Pomona, California. Waste solids removed by carbon adsorption from water during treatment are collected in an incinerator, along with the carbon to which they have adhered. Heated to 1,800 degrees fahrenheit, the wastes are driven off the carbon and out through chimneys, presumably rendered innocuous by having been oxidized to carbon dioxide and water. Regenerated, the carbon can be used over and over. Scientists there plan to install an odor device on the incinerator if tests show that one is needed.

Impurities accumulated by a number of other treatment processes may prove more difficult to handle. It has been suggested for a long time that many wastes may profitably be marketed, but in most cases the cost of processing and shipping these wastes (for use as fertilizers, etc.) is higher than their resale value. However, some waste solids can be used for landfill; still others can be taken 30 miles or more out to sea on barges and dumped or, in inland areas, can be disposed of in high-pressure injection wells ten thousand feet and more beneath the ground. One imaginative school of thought envisages the creation of great underground cavities by nuclear explosions, into which all of our waste solids will be neatly packed.

"We'll do anything with these wastes," Dr. Stephan says, "except dump them into the rivers."

This sentiment, if widely shared a hundred years ago, would have saved America considerable grief.

Appendix I: A Summary of Federal Water Pollution Control Legislation

(*Reprinted from a Staff Report to the Committee on Public Works, United States Senate*)

PRIOR ACTS

Statutory definition of the Federal role and responsibility in water pollution control has evolved over a 60-year span. During this period, more than a hundred bills on this subject were introduced, none of which became law. Until the enactment of the Water Pollution Control Act of 1948, the only Federal role in water pollution was contained in three acts—the Rivers and Harbors Act of 1899, the Public Health Service Act of 1912, and the Oil Pollution Act of 1924.

A section of the Rivers and Harbors Act of 1899 (33 U.S.C. 407) prohibited the discharge or deposit into any navigable waters of any refuse matter except that which flowed in a liquid state from streets and sewers. This provision, designed primarily to prevent impediments to navigation, constituted the first specific Federal water pollution control legislation. Human health factors in water pollution received attention in the Public Health Service Act of 1912 which contained provisions authorizing investigations of water pollution related to the diseases and impairments of man. The Oil Pollution Act of 1924 was enacted to control oil discharges in coastal waters damaging to aquatic life, harbors and docks, and recreational facilities.

Efforts to obtain comprehensive Federal water pollution control legislation continued, however, and were almost successful on three separate occasions in 1936, 1938, and 1940. These efforts were interrupted by World War II, but were renewed in 1947, and culminated in the enactment by the 80th Congress of the Water Pollution Control Act of 1948 (Public Law 845, 80th Cong.). This law was admittedly experimental and initially limited to a trial period of 5 years, after which it was to be reviewed and revised on the basis of experience. This 5-year period was extended for an additional 3 years to June 30, 1956, by Public Law 579, 82d Congress.

THE FEDERAL WATER POLLUTION CONTROL ACT OF 1956

Comprehensive water pollution control legislation of a permanent nature was finally enacted by the 84th Congress with the passage and approval on July 9, 1956, of the Federal Water Pollution Control Act, Public Law 660, 84th Congress. The 1956 act extended and strengthened the 1948 law, which expired on June 30, 1956, and was administered by the Surgeon General of the Public Health Service under the supervision and direction of the Secretary of Health, Education and Welfare. The Act:

1. Reaffirmed the policy of Congress to recognize, preserve, and protect the primary responsibilities and rights of the States in preventing and controlling water pollution;

2. Authorized continued Federal-State cooperation in the development of comprehensive programs for the control of water pollution;

3. Authorized increased technical assistance to States and intensified and broadened research by using the research potential of universities and other institutions outside of Government;

4. Authorized collection and dissemination of basic data on water quality relating to water pollution prevention and control;

5. Directed the Surgeon General to continue to encourage interstate compacts and uniform State laws;

6. Authorized grants to States and interstate agencies up to $3 million a year for the next 5 years for water pollution control activities;

7. Authorized Federal grants of $50 million a year (up to an aggregate of $500 million) for the construction of municipal sewage treatment works, the amount for any one project not to exceed 30 percent of cost, or $250,000, whichever is smaller;

8. Modified and simplified procedures governing Federal abatement actions against interstate pollution;

9. Authorized the appointment of a Water Pollution Control Advisory Board; and

10. Authorized a cooperative program to control pollution from Federal installations.

FEDERAL WATER POLLUTION CONTROL ACT AMENDMENTS OF 1961

Proposals to amend the Federal Water Pollution Control Act to provide for a still more effective program of water pollution control were introduced early in the 1st session of the 87th Congress, and received the endorsement of President Kennedy in his message on natural resources of February 23, 1961. The Congress enacted and President Kennedy signed into law the Federal Water Pollution Control Act Amendments of 1961, Public Law 87-88, on July 20, 1961. The 1961 Amendments improved and strengthened the act by—

1. Extending Federal authority to enforce abatement of intrastate as well as interstate pollution of interstate or navigable waters and strengthening enforcement procedures;

2. Increasing the authorized annual $50 million Federal financial assistance to municipalities for construction of waste treatment works to $80 million in 1962, $90 million in 1963, and $100 million for each of the 4 following fiscal years 1964-67; raising the single grant limitation from $250,000 to $600,000; and providing for grants to communities combining in a joint project up to a limit of $2,400,000;

3. Intensifying research toward more effective methods of pollution control; authorizing for this purpose annual appropriations of $5 million up to an aggregate of $25 million and authorizing the establishment of field laboratory and research facilities in, among others, seven specified major areas of the Nation;

4. Extending for 7 years until June 30, 1968, and increasing Federal financial support of State and interstate water pollution control programs by raising the annual appropriations authorization from $3 to $5 million;

5. Authorizing the inclusion of storage for regulating streamflow for the purpose of water quality control in the survey or planning of Federal reservoirs and impoundments; and

6. Designating the Secretary of Health, Education and Welfare to administer the act.

SCOPE OF THE FEDERAL WATER POLLUTION CONTROL PROGRAM

Four major points need to be considered in reviewing the broad scope of the program contained in the Federal Water Pollution Control Act as amended:

1. The act makes it clear that there is to be a strong Federal role in water pollution control;

2. The provisions of the act make it mandatory that the Secretary carry out certain of the specified programs;

3. The act provides for broad water quality control responsibilities for all water uses; and

4. The act assigns to the Department the primary Federal responsibilities for water pollution control.

The programs authorized and directed to be carried out by the act provide a broad base for dealing with both the water resources and the health aspects of water pollution prevention and control.

Appendix II: State Water Pollution Control Agencies

STATE	AGENCY AND ADDRESS
ALABAMA	Water Improvement Commission State Office Building Montgomery, Ala.
ALASKA	Division of Health Department of Health and Welfare Alaska Office Building Juneau, Alaska
ARIZONA	State Department of Health State Office Building Phoenix, Ariz.
ARKANSAS	State Water Pollution Control Commission 921 West Markham Little Rock, Ark.
CALIFORNIA	State Water Quality Control Board Room 316, 1227 O St. Sacramento, Calif.
COLORADO	State Department of Public Health 4210 East 11th Ave. Denver, Colo.
CONNECTICUT	Water Resources Commission 650 Main St. Hartford, Conn.

STATE	AGENCY AND ADDRESS
DELAWARE	State of Delaware Water Pollution Commission Federal and D Streets State Health Building Dover, Delaware
DISTRICT OF COLUMBIA	District of Columbia Department of Public Health 401 3rd St. NW Washington, D.C.
FLORIDA	State Board of Health 1217 Pearl St. Jacksonville, Fla.
GEORGIA	Georgia Department of Public Health State Office Building Atlanta, Ga.
GUAM	Division of Public Health Territory of Guam P.O. Box 128 Agana, Guam
HAWAII	Hawaii Department of Health Kapuaiwa Building P.O. Box 3378 Honolulu, Hawaii
IDAHO	Idaho Department of Health 715 Idaho Boise, Idaho
ILLINOIS	State Sanitary Water Board State Office Building 400 South Spring St. Springfield, Ill.
INDIANA	Stream Pollution Control Board State Board of Health 1330 West Michigan St. Indianapolis, Ind.

STATE	AGENCY AND ADDRESS
IOWA	State Department of Health State Office Building Des Moines, Iowa
KANSAS	State Department of Health State Office Building Topeka Ave. at 10th Topeka, Kans.
KENTUCKY	Water Pollution Control Commission State Department of Health 275 E. Main Street Frankfort, Ky.
LOUISIANA	Stream Control Commission P.O. Drawer FC, University Station Baton Rouge, La.
MAINE	Water Improvement Commission Department of Health and Welfare State House Augusta, Maine
MARYLAND	State Department of Health State Office Building 301 West Preston St. Baltimore, Md.
MASSACHUSETTS	Massachusetts Department of Public Health 546 State House Boston, Mass.
MICHIGAN	Water Resources Commission Station B Reniger Building 200 Mill St. Lansing, Mich.
MINNESOTA	Water Pollution Control Commission State Department of Health Building Campus, University of Minnesota Minneapolis, Minn.

STATE	AGENCY AND ADDRESS
MISSISSIPPI	State Board of Health Felix J. Underwood State Board of Health Building P.O. Box 1700 Jackson, Miss.
MISSOURI	State Water Pollution Board 112 West High St. Jefferson City, Mo.
MONTANA	State Board of Health Laboratory Building Helena, Mont.
NEBRASKA	Department of Health State Capitol Building Lincoln, Nebr.
NEVADA	State Department of Health Division of Public Health 790 Sutro Street Reno, Nev.
NEW HAMPSHIRE	Water Pollution Commission 61 South Spring St. Concord, N.H.
NEW JERSEY	State Department of Health 129 East Hanover St. Trenton, N.J.
NEW MEXICO	New Mexico Department of Public Health 408 Galister Street Santa Fe, N. Mex.
NEW YORK	State Department of Health 84 Holland Ave. Albany, N.Y.
NORTH CAROLINA	State Stream Sanitation Committee State Department of Water Resources P.O. Box 9392 North McDowell St. Raleigh, N.C.

STATE	AGENCY AND ADDRESS
NORTH DAKOTA	State Department of Health Capitol Building Bismarck, N. Dak.
OHIO	Water Pollution Control Board 306 Ohio Departments Building Columbus, Ohio
OKLAHOMA	State Department of Health 3400 Block of North Eastern Oklahoma City, Okla.
OREGON	State Board of Health 1400 Southwest 5th Ave. Portland, Ore.
PENNSYLVANIA	Sanitary Water Board Pennsylvania Department of Health State Capitol Health and Welfare Building Harrisburg, Pa.
PUERTO RICO	Department of Health Ponce de Leon Ave. San Juan, P.R.
RHODE ISLAND	Department of Health State Office Building Providence, R.I.
SOUTH CAROLINA	State Water Pollution Control Authority Room 417, Wade Hampton Building Columbia, S.C.
SOUTH DAKOTA	Committee on Water Pollution State Capitol Pierre, S. Dak.
TENNESSEE	Stream Pollution Control Board Cordell Hull Building 6th Ave. North Nashville, Tenn.

STATE	AGENCY AND ADDRESS
TEXAS	State Department of Health 1100 West 49th St. Austin, Tex.
UTAH	Water Pollution Control Board 45 South Fort Douglas Blvd. Salt Lake City, Utah
VERMONT	Vermont Department of Water Resources State Office Building Montpelier, Vt.
VIRGINIA	State Water Control Board 415 West Franklin St. P.O. Box 5285 Richmond, Va.
VIRGIN ISLANDS	Virgin Islands Department of Health Charlotte Amalie St. Thomas, V.I.
WASHINGTON	State Pollution Control Commission Room 409, Public Health Building Olympia, Wash.
WEST VIRGINIA	Division of Water Resources Department of Natural Resources 1709 Washington St. East Charleston, W. Va.
WISCONSIN	State Committee on Water Pollution State Office Building Madison, Wis.
WYOMING	State Department of Public Health State Office Building Cheyenne, Wyo.

Index